A Level Physics for OCR

A

Year 1 and AS

Gurinder Chadha

OXFORD
UNIVERSITY PRESS

OXFORD
UNIVERSITY PRESS

Great Clarendon Street, Oxford, OX2 6DP, United Kingdom

Oxford University Press is a department of the University of Oxford. It furthers the University's objective of excellence in research, scholarship, and education by publishing worldwide. Oxford is a registered trade mark of Oxford University Press in the UK and in certain other countries

British Library Cataloguing in Publication Data
Data available

978-0-19-835219-8

10 9 8 7 6 5 4 3 2 1

Paper used in the production of this book is a natural, recyclable product made from wood grown in sustainable forests. The manufacturing process conforms to the environmental regulations of the country of origin.

Printed in Great Britain by Bell and Bain Ltd. Glasgow.

Artwork by Q2A Media

AS/A Level course structure

This book has been written to support students studying for OCR AS Physics A and for students in their first year of studying for OCR A Level Physics A. It covers the AS modules from the specification, the content of which will also be examined at A Level. The modules covered are shown in the contents list, which also shows you the page numbers for the main topics within each module. If you are studying for OCR AS Physics A, you will only need to know the content in the shaded box.

AS exam

A level exam

Year 1 content

1 Development of practical skills in physics
2 Foundations in physics
3 Forces and motion
4 Electrons, waves, and photons

Year 2 content

5 Newtonian world and astrophysics
6 Particles and medical physics

A Level exams will cover content from Year 1 and Year 2 and will be at a higher demand.

Contents

How to use this book

This book contains many different features. Each feature is designed to support and develop the skills you will need for your examinations, as well as foster and stimulate your interest in physics.

 Worked example

Step-by-step worked solutions.

Common misconception

Common misunderstandings clarified.

Maths skills

A focus on maths skills.

Model answers

Sample answers to exam-style questions.

Summary Questions

1   These are short questions at the end of each topic.

2   They test your understanding of the topic and allow you to apply the knowledge and skills you have acquired.

3   The questions are ramped in order of difficulty. Lower-demand questions have a paler background, with the higher-demand questions having a darker background. Try to attempt every question you can, to help you achieve your best in the exams.

Specification references

→   At the beginning of each topic, there are specification references to allow you to monitor your progress.

Revision tips

Prompts to help you with your understanding and revision.

Synoptic link

These highlight the key areas where topics relate to each other. As you go through your course, knowing how to link different areas of physics together becomes increasingly important. Many exam questions, particularly at A Level, will require you to bring together your knowledge from different areas.

Chapter 13 Practice questions

1 Electromagnetic radiation incident on metal ejects electrons from the surface of the metal.

 Which statement about the kinetic energy (KE) of the electrons is correct?

 A The electrons have the same KE.

 B The maximum KE of the electrons depends on the intensity.

 C The KE of electrons is always greater than the work function.

 D The maximum KE depends on the incident wavelength.   (1 mark)

2 What is the typical energy of a photon of infrared radiation?

 A 4×10^{-24} J   C 4×10^{-19} J

 B 4×10^{-20} J   D 4×10^{-17} J   (1 mark)

3 The energy of a photon is related to the wavelength λ or the frequency f of the electromagnetic radiation.

 Which graph will produce a straight line?

 A E against f B E against λ C $E\lambda$ against f D Ef against λ (1 mark)

4 Electrons accelerated through a potential difference V have a de Broglie wavelength λ.

 What is the wavelength of electrons accelerated through a potential difference of $4V$?

 A $\frac{\lambda}{4}$ B $\frac{\lambda}{2}$ C 2λ D 4λ (1 mark)

5 a State what is meant by the photoelectric effect.   (1 mark)

 b Electromagnetic radiation incident on a metal ejects electrons from its surface.

  Explain this observation in terms of photons and electrons.   (3 marks)

 c A researcher is investigating photoelectric effect using a new material.

  Figure 1 shows a graph of maximum kinetic energy KE_{max} of the photoelectrons against frequency f of the incident electromagnetic radiation.

  i Explain why the graph is linear.   (2 marks)

  ii Use Figure 1 to determine the work function of the material in eV.   (4 marks)

  iii Use your answer to (ii) to determine the threshold frequency. (2 marks)

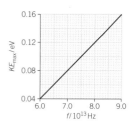

▲ Figure 1

6 The work function of a metal is 3.7 eV. The metal is charged negatively and then it is illuminated with electromagnetic waves of wavelength 300 nm. Photoelectrons are emitted from the surface of the metal.

 a Explain the term work function.   (1 mark)

 b Calculate the maximum kinetic energy, in eV, of the photoelectrons.   (4 marks)

 c Calculate the longest wavelength of electromagnetic radiation that will produce photoelectric effect.   (2 marks)

7 a Explain what is meant by the de Broglie wavelength of an electron.   (2 marks)

 b Fast-electrons can be used to probe into the structure of nuclei. Such electrons have a de Broglie wavelength of about 2.0×10^{-15} m.

  Calculate the momentum of the electrons.   (2 marks)

 c Briefly described an experiment that confirms that electrons behave as waves.   (3 marks)

Module 2 Foundations of physics
Chapter 2 Foundations of physics

In this chapter you will learn about ...

- ☐ SI units
- ☐ Base units
- ☐ Derived units
- ☐ Prefixes
- ☐ Scalars and vectors
- ☐ Vector triangles
- ☐ Resultant vectors
- ☐ Resolving a vector
- ☐ Components of a vector

FOUNDATIONS OF PHYSICS
2.1 Quantities and units
2.2 Derived units
Specification reference: 2.1.1, 2.1.2

2.1 Quantities and units

A **physical quantity** in physics means a measurement of something and its unit.

A physical quantity has a number followed by a unit. For example, the length of a mobile phone is 0.125 m. There are a few exceptions where a physical quantity does not have a unit. Examples of this include tensile strain and efficiency.

Quantities and SI base units

There are many different units for length – inch, foot, yard, mile, and so on. In physics we agree to work with the metre (m). The metre is an example from a list of seven internationally agreed base units, or SI units (*Système International d'Unités*). Table 1 summarises the six physical quantities and their SI base units you need to know.

▼ **Table 1** *Physical quantities and their SI base units*

Physical quantity	SI base unit
length	metre (m)
mass	kilogram (kg)
time	second (s)
electric current	ampere (A)
temperature	kelvin (K)
amount of substance	mole (mol)

Prefixes

To cope with the very large and very small numbers that are used in the study of physics, it is often useful to write numbers as powers of ten. Prefixes are used as abbreviations for some powers of ten – you need to learn the prefixes listed in Table 2.

The sub-multiples (for smaller measurements) are femto, pico, nano, micro, milli, centi, and deci, and the multiples (for larger measurements) are kilo, mega, giga, tera, and peta.

▼ **Table 2** *Important prefixes*

Prefix name	Prefix symbol	Factor
peta	P	10^{15}
tera	T	10^{12}
giga	G	10^{9}
mega	M	10^{6}
kilo	k	10^{3}
deci	d	10^{-1}
centi	c	10^{-2}
milli	m	10^{-3}
micro	μ	10^{-6}
nano	n	10^{-9}
pico	p	10^{-12}
femto	f	10^{-15}

Common misconception

The prefix mega is *capital* M and the milli is *lower case* m. If you have poor writing, then these two prefixes can look the same. Just be vigilant.

Maths: Standard form or scientific notation

A number in standard notation is written as $n \times 10^{m}$, where n is a number greater than 1 but less than 10 and m is a positive or a negative integer. A distance of 320 km in metres may be written as 320×10^{3} m but in standard form it must be written as 3.2×10^{5} m.

Worked example: Speed

Speed is defined as the rate of change of distance. Calculate the speed of a particle that travels a distance of 9.1 Mm in a time of 50 ms.

Step 1: Write the magnitude of each quantity by substituting for the prefix.

$$\text{distance} = 9.1 \times 10^6 \, \text{m} \qquad \text{time} = 50 \times 10^{-3} \, \text{s}$$

Step 2: Calculate the speed and write your answer in standard notation.

$$\text{speed} = \frac{\text{distance}}{\text{time}} = \frac{9.1 \times 10^6}{50 \times 10^{-3}} = 1.82 \times 10^8 \, \text{m s}^{-1} = 1.8 \times 10^8 \, \text{m s}^{-1} \, (2 \, \text{s.f.})$$

Note: The data is given to 2 significant figures (s.f.), so the final answer must also be written to 2 s.f.

2.2 Derived units

You have already met an example of a derived unit: m s^{-1}. This unit for speed can be determined from the equation for speed and the base units for length and time. Since speed $= \frac{\text{distance}}{\text{time}}$, the derived unit for speed must be metre (m) divided by second (s). This can be written as m/s, but at advanced level this is written as m s^{-1}.

More on derived units

Table 3 shows some examples of derived units. In each case, the equation used to determine the final units is shown.

▼ **Table 3** *Derived units*

Physical quantity	Equation	Derived unit	
area	area = length × width	m × m	$\rightarrow \text{m}^2$
density	$\text{density} = \dfrac{\text{mass}}{\text{volume}}$	$\dfrac{\text{kg}}{\text{m}^3}$	$\rightarrow \text{kg m}^{-3}$
acceleration	$\text{acceleration} = \dfrac{\text{change in velocity}}{\text{time}}$	$\dfrac{\text{m s}^{-1}}{\text{s}}$	$\rightarrow \text{m s}^{-2}$
force	force = mass × acceleration	$\text{kg} \times \text{m s}^{-2}$	$\rightarrow \text{kg m s}^{-2}$

> **Revision tip: Negative powers**
> In mathematics, $\frac{1}{x^n}$ may be written as x^{-n}. This convention is adopted when writing units. Therefore $\frac{\text{kg}}{\text{m}^3}$ is equivalent to kg m^{-3}.

Summary questions

1   The distance between two towns is 210 km.
    Write this distance in metres.   *(1 mark)*
2   The speed of an electron within a wire is 1.2 mm s^{-1}.
    Write this speed in m s^{-1}.   *(1 mark)*
3   It takes 12 ns for light to travel across a room.
    Write this time in standard form and in seconds.   *(1 mark)*

4   The diameter of an atom is 2.3×10^{-10} m.
    Write this diameter in pm and in nm.   *(2 marks)*
5   Use Table 3 to determine the unit for work done by a force,
    where work done = force × distance travelled in the direction
    of the force.   *(2 marks)*

6   The distance between the Sun and the Earth is 150 Gm and the
    speed of light is 300 Mm s^{-1}.
    Calculate the time taken for light to travel from the Sun to
    the Earth.   *(3 marks)*
7   The area of a sheet of paper is 620 cm^3. Calculate this
    area in m^2.   *(2 marks)*

2.3 Scalar and vector quantities
2.4 Adding vectors

Specification reference: 2.3.1

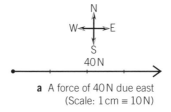

a A force of 40N due east
(Scale: 1cm ≡ 10N)

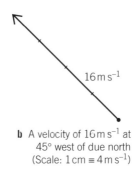

b A velocity of 16ms⁻¹ at
45° west of due north
(Scale: 1cm ≡ 4ms⁻¹)

▲ **Figure 1** *Representing vectors*

> **Revision tip**
> Distance is a scalar and
> displacement is a vector.
>
> Speed is a scalar and velocity
> is a vector.

2.3 Scalar and vector quantities

Many of the physical quantities in physics can be divided into two categories – scalars and vectors. The way we add, or subtract, these quantities is very different, so you must be able to identify whether a quantity is a scalar or a vector.

Scalars

A **scalar quantity** has only magnitude (size).

Distance, speed, time, area, volume, mass, energy, temperature, electrical charge, and frequency are all scalars. Two similar scalar quantities can be added or subtracted in the normal way. For example, if you have a beaker of water on a digital balance, reading 250g, and you add 50g of water to the beaker, the total mass of the beaker and water will now be 300g.

Vectors

A **vector quantity** has both magnitude and direction.

Displacement, velocity, acceleration, momentum, and force are all vectors. A vector can be represented as a line of suitable length drawn in the direction of the vector, see Figure 1.

2.4 Adding vectors

You have to take the directions of the two vectors into account when adding, or subtracting them.

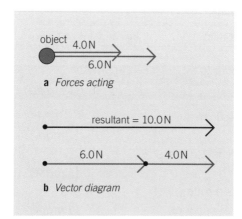

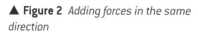

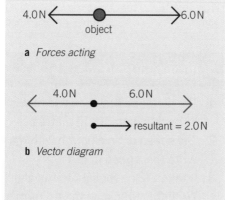

▲ **Figure 2** *Adding forces in the same direction*

▲ **Figure 3** *Adding forces in opposite directions*

Figure 2 shows two forces acting on an object in the same direction and Figure 3 shows two forces acting in opposite directions. The resultant is just a matter of adding or subtracting the magnitudes.

What happens when the forces are at an angle to each other? This is where you have to carefully construct a vector triangle force – the resultant can either be determined from a scale drawing or by calculation.

Vector triangle

Figure 4 shows two forces, at right angles to each other, acting on an object and a vector triangle used to determine the resultant force. The vector triangle can be drawn to scale using the following rules:

- Choose a suitable scale.
- Draw a line to represent the first vector.
- Draw a line to represent the second vector from the end of the first vector.
- The magnitude and direction of the resultant vector can be found by drawing a line from the start to the end.

You can use these rules for any other vector and even when the angle between the vectors is not 90°.

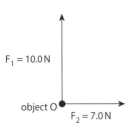

▲ **Figure 4a** *Two forces acting on an object*

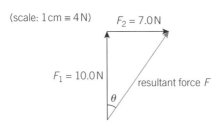

▲ **Figure 4b** *The vector triangle to determine the resultant force*

 Worked example: Resultant force

Use Figure 4b to determine the magnitude and direction of the resultant force.

Step 1: Draw a clearly labelled vector triangle.

This has already been done for you in Figure 4b.

Step 2: Use Pythagoras' theorem to determine the magnitude of the resultant force F.

$$F^2 = F_1^2 + F_2^2 = 10.0^2 + 7.0^2$$

$$F = \sqrt{149} = 12\,N$$

Note: The resultant force must be the largest force, and it is.

Step 3: Calculate the angle using trigonometry.

$$\tan\theta = \frac{7.0}{10.0} = 0.700$$

$$\theta = \tan^{-1}(0.700) = 35°\ (2\ s.f.)$$

Revision tip: Get the mode right

Make sure that your calculator is in the correct mode when determining the angle. An angle in radians is not the same as the angle in degrees.

Maths: Pythagoras' theorem

This theorem only works when one of the internal angles of the triangle is 90°. You can use the sine and the cosine rules when this is not the case. All this information is provided for you in the Data, formula, and relationships booklet.

Summary questions

1. Name two scalar quantities and two vector quantities. *(2 marks)*
2. Suggest what is wrong with the calculation 13 kg + 100 N. *(1 mark)*

3. A car is travelling at 20 m s^{-1} on a circular track. The wind speed is 5.0 m s^{-1}.
   Calculate the maximum and minimum magnitudes of the resultant velocity of the car. *(2 marks)*
4. Two forces of the same magnitude of 4.0 N and at right angles to each other are added together.
   Draw a vector triangle. *(2 marks)*

5. Calculate the resultant force for the two forces in Q4. *(2 marks)*
6. A swimmer can swim at 1.8 m s^{-1} in still water.
   He aims to swim *directly* across a river flowing at 1.0 m s^{-1}.
   a. Draw a labelled vector triangle. *(2 marks)*
   b. Calculate the magnitude of the resultant velocity of the swimmer. *(2 marks)*

2.5 Resolving vectors
2.6 More on vectors

Specification reference: 2.3.1

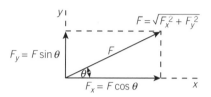

▲ **Figure 1** *Resolving a vector into two mutually perpendicular components*

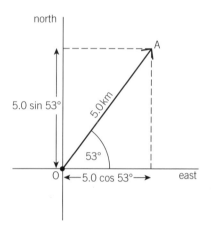

▲ **Figure 2** *The components of a displacement*

2.5 Resolving vectors

It is often useful to resolve, or split up, a vector into two components at right angles to each other. This process is particularly useful when analysing the motion of a projectile on the surface of the Earth – the horizontal and vertical velocities are independent of each other.

Components of a vector

Figure 1 shows a vector, in this case a force of magnitude F, being resolved in the x- and y-directions. You can use the rules below for any vector (velocity, acceleration, etc).

● The components of the vector are:
  ● $F_x = F\cos\theta$ in the x-direction and $F_y = F\sin\theta$ in the y-direction.
● The magnitude F of the vector can be determined using $F^2 = F_x^2 + F_y^2$.
● The angle θ made by the vector to the horizontal can be determined using $\tan\theta = \dfrac{F_y}{F_x}$.

Figure 2 shows a displacement of 5.0 km resolved into its two components. The displacement due east is 30 km and 40 km in the north direction.

> **Maths: Cos and sin**
>
> It is useful to know that $\cos(90 - \theta) = \sin\theta$. Try this on your calculator.
>
> When the x-component is $F\cos\theta$, then the y-component is equivalent to $F\cos(90 - \theta)$.

> **Revision tip: Just remember the cosine**
>
> In general, the component of a force (or any other vector) at an angle θ is given by $F\cos\theta$.

2.6 More on vectors
Adding non-perpendicular vectors

Vectors are often not at right angles to each other. You can still determine the resultant vector using the four bulleted rules in Topic 2.4, Adding vectors, by drawing a vector triangle. You will need a very sharp pencil and be able to measure length and angle size accurately, see Figure 3.

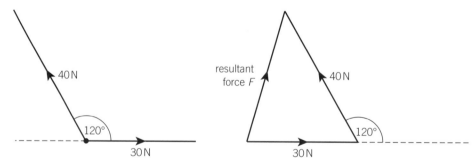

▲ **Figure 3** *You can draw a scaled vector triangle to determine the resultant vector*

You can replicate the process illustrated in Figure 3 to determine any resultant vector, including velocity and momentum.

Calculations

You can also use the sine rule and the cosine rule to determine the magnitude and direction of the resultant vector. A decent sketch of a vector triangle is necessary before you can do any calculations. See the worked example below.

Model answers: Using the cosine rule

Use the cosine rule to show that the magnitude of the resultant force *F* in Figure 3 is 36 N.

Answer

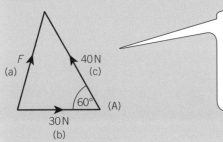

A clearly labelled vector triangle is essential and you need to know the angle 'opposite' to the 'side' *F* of this triangle for the cosine rule.

cosine rule: $a^2 = b^2 + c^2 - 2bc \cos A$

$a^2 = b^2 + c^2 - 2bc \cos A$

Therefore

$F^2 = 30^2 + 40^2 - 2 \times 30 \times 40 \times \cos 60°$

It is important to show all your working.

$F = \sqrt{1300}$

$F = 36$ N

The data is given to 2 s.f. It is good practice to write the final answer also to 2 s.f.

Note: In order to calculate any of the other internal angles of the triangle, you can use the sine rule

$$\frac{a}{\sin A} = \frac{b}{\sin B} = \frac{c}{\sin C}$$

Subtracting two vectors

Subtracting two vectors is very much like adding two vectors, except you reverse the direction of one of the vectors. This is illustrated in Figure 4. Where you want the resultant vector of **A** – **B**, you can apply the following rules:

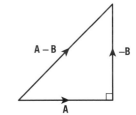

- Draw a line to represent the vector **A**.

- Draw a line in the opposite direction to represent the vector −**B** from the end of the vector **A**.

▲ **Figure 4** *Subtracting vectors*

- The magnitude and direction of the resultant vector can be found by drawing a line from the start to the end.

Summary questions

1 A rocket has a velocity of 300 m s⁻¹ at an angle of 65° to the horizontal. Calculate the horizontal and vertical components of this velocity. (*2 marks*)

2 A ball rolls down a frictionless ramp. The acceleration of free fall is 9.81 m s⁻². The ramp makes an angle of 30° to the vertical. Calculate the acceleration of the ball down the ramp. (*1 mark*)

3 A force of magnitude *F* is at an angle of 50° to the horizontal. The vertical component to the force is 100 N. Calculate the magnitude of *F*. (*2 marks*)

4 Calculate the resultant force in each case shown in Figure 5. (*4 marks*)

5 Two forces of magnitudes 100 N and 200 N act on an object. The angle between the forces is 110°. Calculate the magnitude of the resultant force. (*3 marks*)

6 In Q5, the direction of the 200 N is reversed. Calculate the magnitude of the resultant force now. (*3 marks*)

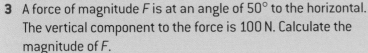

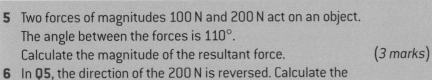

▲ **Figure 5**

1 Which is the correct definition for a scalar quantity?
   A scalar quantity ......

   A has no units.

   B has direction only.

   C has magnitude only.

   D has magnitude and direction. *(1 mark)*

2 What is force measured in base units?

   A N

   B kg

   C $kg\,s^2\,m^{-1}$

   D $kg\,m\,s^{-2}$ *(1 mark)*

3 An object experiences two forces of magnitudes 3.2 N and 5.0 N. The forces are at right angles to each other.

   What is the magnitude of the resultant force on the object?

   A 3.8 N

   B 5.9 N

   C 15 N

   D 35 N *(1 mark)*

4 The horizontal component of a 10.0 N force is 8.0 N.

   What is the angle between the 10.0 N force and the horizontal?

   A 0°

   B 37°

   C 39°

   D 53° *(1 mark)*

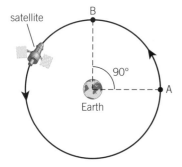

▲ **Figure 1**

5 Figure 1 shows a satellite orbiting round the Earth at a distance of 2.0×10^7 m from its centre. The satellite has constant speed.

   a Explain why the velocity of the satellite is not constant in its orbit. *(1 mark)*

   b The satellite travels from point A to point B. Calculate:

      i the distance travelled by the satellite; *(2 marks)*

      ii the displacement of the satellite from point A. *(3 marks)*

6 Figure 2 shows the two forces acting on a block of wood placed on a smooth ramp.

   The weight W of the block is 8.0 N and the normal contact force N is 6.9 N.

   a Explain why N has no affect on the motion of the block down the ramp. *(1 mark)*

   b Calculate the component of the weight down the ramp. *(1 mark)*

   c Draw a labelled vector diagram and determine the resultant force acting on the block. *(4 marks)*

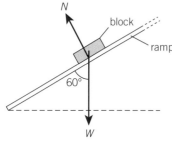

▲ **Figure 2**

Module 3 Forces and Motion
Chapter 3 Motion

In this chapter you will learn about ...

- [ ] Speed

- [ ] Distance—time graphs

- [ ] Velocity

- [ ] Displacement-time graphs

- [ ] Acceleration

- [ ] Velocity-time graphs

- [ ] Equations of motion (*suvat* equations)

- [ ] Thinking, braking, and stopping distances

- [ ] Free fall and *g*

- [ ] Projectiles

3 MOTION
3.1 Distance and speed
3.2 Displacement and velocity

Specification reference: 3.1.1

3.1 Distance and speed

You can measure the distance travelled by an object using a metre rule or a measuring tape. The speed of an object is related to distance and time.

Speed

Speed is defined as the rate of change of distance. You can use the following word equation to determine the average speed v of an object:

$$\text{average speed} = \frac{\text{total distance travelled}}{\text{time taken}}$$

or

$$v = \frac{\Delta x}{\Delta t}$$

where Δx is the total distance travelled in a time Δt. The SI unit for speed is $m\,s^{-1}$. You can also use this equation to determine the **constant** speed of an object and it can be modified to determine the instantaneous speed of an object, as shown below.

$$v = \frac{\delta x}{\delta t}$$

where δx is the very small distance travelled by the object in a very small time interval δt.

Maths: Change in

The Greek letter capital delta Δ is shorthand for 'change in...'. So Δt means 'change in t'.

In physics lower case δ is used to signify 'very small change in...'.

Maths: Gradient

On a y against x graph, the gradient $= \frac{\text{change in } y}{\text{change in } x}$

$$\text{speed at Y} = \frac{PQ}{QR} = \frac{192-52}{20}$$
$$= 7.0\,m\,s^{-1}$$

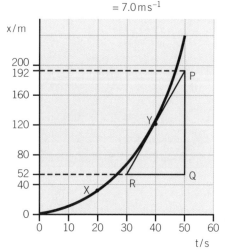

▲ **Figure 1** *You can determine the speed of an object from the gradient of the graph*

🖩 Worked example: Speed

A space probe orbits round a planet in a circular path of radius 5.6×10^5 m at a constant speed. It takes 96 minutes to orbit once round the planet. Calculate the speed of the space probe.

Step 1: Write down all the quantities given in SI units.

$$r = 5.6 \times 10^5 \text{ m} \qquad t = 96 \times 60 = 5.76 \times 10^3 \text{ s}$$

Step 2: Calculate the speed, remembering that the distance is the circumference.

$$v = \frac{\Delta x}{\Delta t} = \frac{2\pi r}{t} = \frac{2\pi \times 5.6 \times 10^5}{5.76 \times 10^3}$$
$$v = 611 \text{ m s}^{-1} \approx 610 \text{ m s}^{-1} \text{ (2 s.f.)}$$

Distance–time graph

The motion of an object can be displayed on a distance–time (x–t) graph.

● The speed of the object at time t can be determined from the gradient of the graph at this time t.

● For a curved distance–time graph, the speed can be calculated by determining the gradient of a tangent drawn to the graph, see Figure 1.

3.2 Displacement and velocity

Displacement is defined as the distance in a given direction.

It is a vector with both magnitude and direction. The magnitude of a displacement is the same as the distance travelled when an object travels in a straight line in a given direction, for example, a falling apple.

Velocity

Velocity is defined as the rate of change of displacement. The SI unit for velocity is the same as that for speed. The word equation for velocity is

$$\text{velocity} = \frac{\text{change in displacement}}{\text{time taken}}$$

The equation for velocity v is

$$v = \frac{\Delta s}{\Delta t}$$

where Δs is the change in displacement and Δt is the time taken.

Displacement–time graph

The motion of an object can be displayed on a displacement–time (s–t) graph.

- The gradient of an s–t graph is equal to the velocity v of the object.
- A negative gradient represents motion in the opposite direction.
- For a curved s–t graph, the instantaneous velocity is found by drawing a tangent to the graph and then determining the gradient of this tangent.

Summary questions

1   Calculate the average speed in m s^{-1} of a trolley travelling a distance of 120 cm in a time of 3.4 s.   *(1 mark)*
2   A car is travelling at a constant speed of 20 m s^{-1}. Calculate the distance travelled in 0.40 hours.   *(2 marks)*

3   Figure 2 shows the displacement–time graph for three objects **A**, **B**, and **C**. Describe the motion of each object.   *(3 marks)*
4   A car travels 2.0 km due north for 30 minutes at a constant velocity. Then it travels 1.0 km due south for another 30 minutes at a different constant velocity.
    Sketch a displacement–time (s–t) graph for the car.   *(2 marks)*

5   An electron travels in a circular path of radius 2.0 cm at a constant speed of 5.0×10^5 m s^{-1}.
    Calculate the time taken by the electron to complete one orbit.   *(2 marks)*
6   Figure 3 shows the displacement–time graph for a ball thrown vertically upwards on the Earth's surface.
    a   Describe the motion of the ball at time $t = 0.5$ s and time $t = 1.5$ s.   *(2 marks)*
    b   What is the magnitude of the velocity of the ball at $t = 1.0$ s? Explain your answer.   *(2 marks)*

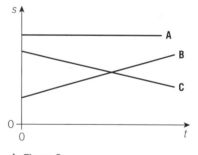

▲ Figure 2

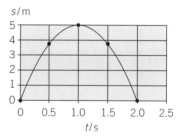

▲ Figure 3

3.3 Acceleration
3.4 More on velocity–time graphs

3.3 Acceleration

Acceleration is a vector quantity – it has both magnitude and direction. An object is accelerating when its speed is increasing and it is decelerating when its speed decreases. An object will also have an acceleration when its direction of travel changes.

Defining acceleration

Acceleration is defined as the rate of change of velocity. In SI units, acceleration is measured in metre per second squared ($m\,s^{-2}$). The word equation for acceleration is

$$\text{acceleration} = \frac{\text{change in velocity}}{\text{time taken}}$$

The equation for acceleration a is

$$a = \frac{\Delta v}{\Delta t}$$

where Δv is the change in velocity in $m\,s^{-1}$ and Δt is the time taken in s.

You can also write this as

$$a = \frac{v - u}{t}$$

where u is the initial velocity, v is the final velocity, and t is the time taken for the change in velocity.

> **Common misconception**
>
> Do not define acceleration as 'the rate of change of speed'.

> **Maths: Change in velocity**
>
> The Greek delta Δ is shorthand for 'a change in'. So Δv means a change in velocity.

> **Revision tip: Signs**
>
> A positive acceleration means increasing velocity.
>
> A negative acceleration means decreasing velocity or a deceleration.

> **Worked example: Deceleration**
>
> A car is travelling on a straight road. The driver applies the brakes. The velocity of the car changes from $30\,m\,s^{-1}$ to $12\,m\,s^{-1}$ in a time of $5.0\,s$. Calculate the acceleration of the car.
>
> **Step 1:** Write down the known and unknown quantities.
>
> $u = 30\,m\,s^{-1}$ $v = 12\,m\,s^{-1}$ $t = 5.0\,s$ $a = ?$
>
> **Step 2:** Write down the equation, substitute and solve.
>
> $$a = \frac{v - u}{t} = \frac{12 - 30}{5.0} = -3.6\,m\,s^{-2}\ \text{(2 s.f.)}$$
>
> The minus sign means the car is decelerating.
> The magnitude of the deceleration is $3.6\,m\,s^{-2}$ (2 s.f.).

3.4 Velocity–time graphs

You can interpret the motion of an object from its velocity v against time t (or v–t) graph.

Information from v–t graphs

● The gradient of a v–t graph is equal to the acceleration a of the object.

● The area under a v–t graph is equal to the displacement s of the object.

A positive gradient shows that the velocity of the object is increasing. A negative gradient shows that the object is decelerating. You can calculate the instantaneous acceleration of an object by drawing a tangent to the graph and then determining the gradient of this tangent, see Figure 1.

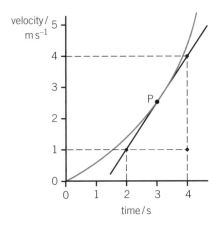

▲ **Figure 1** *The acceleration a can be determined from the gradient of the tangent drawn at point P*

Model answers: Analysing motion

Figure 2 shows the v–t graph for an object travelling in a straight line.

Determine:

a the acceleration of the object at time t = 3.0 s;

b the total distance travelled in 6.0 s.

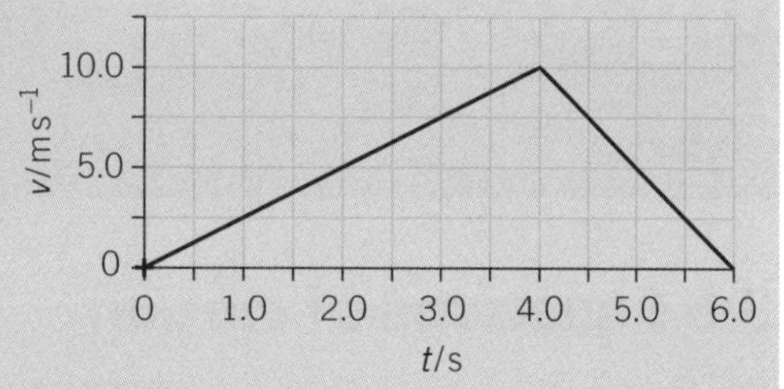

▲ **Figure 2**

Answer

a The acceleration is the gradient at t = 3.0 s

$$a = \frac{\Delta v}{\Delta t} = \frac{10.0 - 0}{4.0} = 2.5 \, \text{m s}^{-2}$$

> The object has uniform acceleration from t = 0 to t = 4.0 s.
>
> This is a well-structured answer – the equation first, then the substitution and finally the answer quoted to 2 significant figures.

b The area under the graph is equal to the displacement s, which is the same as the distance travelled.

> This opening statement makes the physics very clear.

s = area of triangle

$$s = \frac{1}{2} \times 6.0 \times 10.0 = 30 \, \text{m}$$

> You can also calculate the total area by adding the areas of the two smaller triangles as follows:
>
> $$s = \left(\frac{1}{2} \times 4.0 \times 10.0\right) + \left(\frac{1}{2} \times 2.0 \times 10.0\right) = 30 \, \text{m}$$
>
> The answer is the same.
>
> The method shown in this model answer is shorter and neater.

Maths: Improving accuracy

On a y–x graph, the gradient is calculated by dividing Δy by Δx.

To improve accuracy, always use a large 'triangle' to determine the gradient.

Revision tip

Uniform acceleration means *constant* acceleration.

Summary questions

1 Describe the motion of an object with the v–t graph shown in Figure 3a, 3b, and 3c. (3 marks)

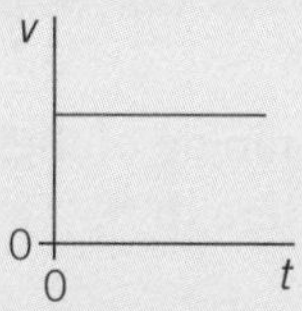

▲ **Figure 3a**

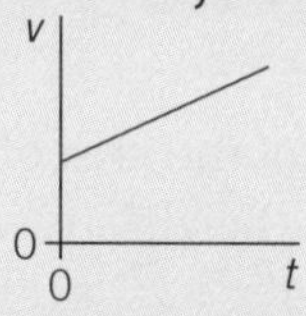

▲ **Figure 3b**

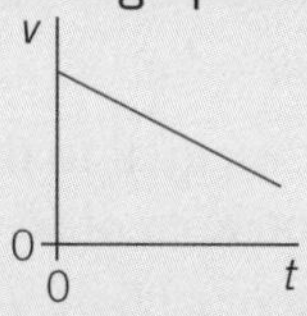

▲ **Figure 3c**

2 An aircraft can change its velocity from 100 m s⁻¹ to 320 m s⁻¹ in 20 s. Calculate the acceleration of the aircraft. (2 marks)

3 A rocket has a constant acceleration of 3.0 m s⁻².
Calculate the change in its velocity in a time interval of 1.5 minutes. (2 marks)

4 A ball bounces off a wall. The change in velocity of the ball is 10 m s⁻¹ and acceleration of the ball when in contact with the wall is 400 m s⁻². Calculate the time for which the ball is in contact with the wall. (2 marks)

5 Use Figure 1 to determine the instantaneous acceleration of the object at time t = 3.0 s. (2 marks)

6 A cyclist, initially at rest, accelerates uniformly for 10 s and reaches a velocity of 4.0 m s⁻¹ on a straight road. She then travels at this constant velocity for a further period of 35 s. Finally she decelerates uniformly to rest in 5.0 s.
   a Sketch a velocity–time graph for her journey. (3 marks)
   b Calculate the total distance travelled by the cyclist. (3 marks)
   c Calculate the magnitude of the deceleration. (2 marks)

3.5 Equations of motion
3.6 Car stopping distances
Specification reference: 3.1.2

3.5 Equations of motion

The four equations of motions (also known as the *'suvat'* equations) are expressions that can be applied to the motion of an object travelling in a straight line with a constant (or uniform) acceleration. The following labels are used for the quantities:

$s \rightarrow$ displacement (or distance travelled when the direction of travel remains the same)

$u \rightarrow$ initial velocity

$v \rightarrow$ final velocity

$a \rightarrow$ acceleration

$t \rightarrow$ time taken for the change in velocity

The four equations of motion

There are four equations of motion that can be derived from the velocity against time graph shown in Figure 1.

- **Equation 1:** $v = u + at$

  The gradient of the graph is equal to a.

  Therefore $a = \frac{v - u}{t}$. When rearranged, this gives

  $$v = u + at$$

- **Equation 2:** $s = \frac{1}{2}(u + v)t$

  The area under the line graph is equal to the displacement s. This is equal to the area of a trapezium of 'height' t and 'parallel lengths' u and v. Therefore

  $$s = \frac{1}{2}(u + v)t$$

- **Equation 3:** $s = ut + \frac{1}{2}at^2$

  The displacement is equal to the sum of the area of the rectangle of 'height' u and 'length' t and area of triangle of 'height' $(v - u)$ and 'length' t.

  Therefore $s = [u \times t] + \left[\frac{1}{2}(v - u)t\right]$

  However, $v - u = at$ from equation 1. Therefore $s = ut + \frac{1}{2}(at)t$, or simply

  $$s = ut + \frac{1}{2}at^2$$

- **Equation 4:** $v^2 = u^2 + 2as$

  This final equation can be derived from equations 1 and 2.

  From equation 1 we have $t = \frac{v - u}{a}$. When this is substituted into equation 2, we have

  $$s = \frac{1}{2}(v + u) \times \frac{(v - u)}{a} = \frac{v^2 - u^2 - uv + uv}{2a}$$

  Therefore $2as = v^2 - u^2$

  This simplifies to

  $$v^2 = u^2 + 2as$$

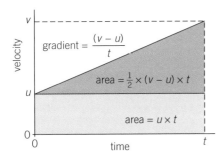

▲ **Figure 1** *The gradient of the graph is equal to acceleration and the area under the graph is equal to displacement*

gradient $= \frac{(v - u)}{t}$

area $= \frac{1}{2} \times (v - u) \times t$

area $= u \times t$

Revision tip: Get the signs right

The acceleration a is a positive number for acceleration and a negative number for deceleration. For an object projected vertically upwards, $a = -9.81\ \text{m s}^{-2}$.

Worked example: Braking car

A car is travelling at a velocity of 31 m s^{-1} on a straight road. The driver applies the brakes. The car comes to rest after travelling a distance of 18 m. Calculate the magnitude of the deceleration of the car.

Step 1: Write down all the quantities given and include the unknown quantity.

$$s = 18\,m \qquad u = 31\,m\,s^{-1} \qquad v = 0 \qquad a = ?$$

Step 2: Identify the correct *suvat* equation, rearrange the equation, substitute the values, and calculate *a*.

$$v^2 = u^2 + 2as$$

$$a = \frac{v^2 - u^2}{2s} = \frac{0^2 - 31^2}{2 \times 18} = -27\,m\,s^{-2}\,(2\,s.f.)$$

The magnitude of the deceleration is 27 m s^{-2} (2 s.f.).

3.6 Car stopping distances

The stopping distance of a car is made up of two components – thinking distance and braking distance.

Stopping distance is defined as the sum of thinking distance and braking distance.

Thinking distance is defined as the distance travelled between the moment the driver sees a reason to stop and the moment when the driver applies the brake.

The **braking distance** is the distance travelled by the car from the instant the brake is applied until the car stops.

*   Thinking distance depends on the initial speed *u* of the car and the 'reaction' time of the driver – thinking distance $\propto u$.

*   Braking distance depends on a number of factors, including the initial speed *u* of the car, the condition of the tyres, brakes and road, and the alertness of the driver – braking distance $\propto u^2$.

Summary questions

1   A stone is thrown vertically upwards at a speed of 15 m s^{-1}. Calculate its velocity after 1.0 s. *(2 marks)*

2   A car is travelling at 5.0 m s^{-1}. It suddenly speeds up for 7.0 s with a constant acceleration of 3.0 m s^{-2}. Calculate the distance travelled by the car in this interval of time. *(2 marks)*

3   Figure 2 shows the *v–t* graph for a car. The driver starts to react at time *t* = 0.
    Calculate the thinking distance, braking distance, and the stopping distance of the car. *(3 marks)*

4   The distance travelled by a car is 80 m as its speed increases from 10 m s^{-1} to 25 m s^{-1}.
    Calculate the time taken to travel this distance. *(3 marks)*

5   A metal ball is dropped from rest from the top of a building 100 m high. Calculate its speed just before it hits the ground below. *(3 marks)*

6   A golf ball is dropped on a hard floor. It hits the floor at a speed of 14 m s^{-1} and bounces back up at a speed of 12 m s^{-1}. It is in contact with the ground for 4.0 ms.
    Calculate the magnitude of the average acceleration of the ball. *(3 marks)*

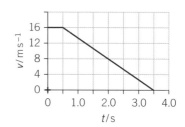

▲ Figure 2

3.7 Free fall and *g*

Specification reference: 3.1.2

3.7 Free fall and *g*

All objects on the surface of the Earth fall with the same acceleration, as long as air resistance is negligible. This acceleration of free fall *g* is equal to 9.81 m s⁻² and is independent of the mass of an object. You can use the equations of motion (see Topic 3.5), to analyse the motion of objects falling freely in the Earth's gravitational field.

Determining acceleration of free fall *g*

Figure 1 shows an arrangement that can be used in the laboratory to determine the acceleration of free fall. A heavy steel ball is dropped from rest from an electromagnet. The distance *h* of fall is measured using a metre rule and the time *t* of fall is determined using a trapdoor and timer arrangement. The experimental value for *g* can be determined by plotting a graph of *h* against t^2.

- Equation of motion used: $s = ut + \frac{1}{2}at^2$, with $u = 0$, $a = g$, and $s = h$

- Comparison with equation for a straight line: $s = \left(\frac{g}{2}\right)t^2$, with $s \rightarrow y$ and $t^2 \rightarrow x$

A graph of *h* against t^2 will be a straight line with a gradient equal to $\frac{g}{2}$. Therefore $g = 2 \times$ gradient

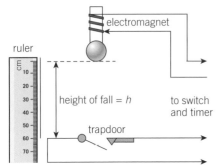

▲ **Figure 1** *Arrangement used to determine the acceleration of free fall*

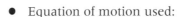

> **Revision tip: Gradients**
>
> Use a large 'triangle' to determine the gradient of a straight line. This will improve the accuracy.

Using light gates and taking pictures

You can determine the speed of a falling object, for example, a metal plate, using a light gate connected to either a timer or a data-logger. This can then be used to calculate a value for *g*. This method of analysis is illustrated in the worked example below.

You can also take stroboscopic images of a falling object. The images of the falling object are taken at regular time intervals. The equation of motion $s = ut + \frac{1}{2}at^2$ can be used to determine *g*.

> ### ▦ Worked example: Analysing data from a light gate and timer
>
> A metal plate of length 9.00 cm is dropped from a height of 1.00 m above a light gate connected to a timer. The metal plate falls vertically through the light gate. The timer records 0.020 s.
>
> **a** Calculate the acceleration of free fall.
>
> **b** Determine the % difference between the experimental value and the accepted value for the acceleration of free fall.
>
> **Step 1:** Calculate the final velocity of the metal plate.
> $$v = \frac{\text{length of plate}}{\text{time taken}} = \frac{0.090}{0.020} = 4.50 \text{ m s}^{-1}$$
>
> **Step 2:** Identify the correct *suvat* equation, rearrange the equation, substitute the values, and calculate *a*.
> $$v^2 = u^2 + 2as, \text{ with } u = 0 \text{ and } a = g$$
> $$g = \frac{v^2}{2s} = \frac{4.50^2}{2 \times 1.00}$$
> $$g = 10.1 \text{ m s}^{-2}$$
>
> **Step 3:** Determine the % difference.
> $$\% \text{ difference} = \frac{10.1 - 9.81}{9.81} \times 100 = 3.0\%$$

Summary questions

1 A rock and a metal ball are dropped on the surface of the Earth. State the acceleration of free fall of each object. *(1 mark)*

2 A heavy metal ball is dropped from rest. Calculate the distance travelled by the ball after 0.30 s. *(2 marks)*

3 The acceleration of free fall on the surface of the Moon is $1.6\ m\,s^{-2}$. Calculate the distance travelled by a ball dropped on the surface of the Moon after 0.30 s. *(2 marks)*

4 An apple falls off a tree from a height of 2.5 m. It takes 0.70 s before it hits the ground below.
Estimate a value for the acceleration of fall. *(3 marks)*

5 A student conducts a free fall experiment in the laboratory using the arrangement shown in Figure 1.
The results are shown below.
height $h = 800 \pm 3$ mm $t = 0.403 \pm 0.002$ s
Determine a value for the acceleration of free fall. *(3 marks)*

6 Figure 2 shows a graph of s against t^2 plotted by a student following an experiment. The distance of fall is s and the time taken is t.
Use Figure 2 to determine a value for g. *(3 marks)*

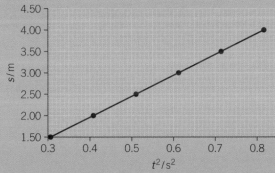

▲ Figure 2

7 Determine the absolute uncertainty in the value for the acceleration of free fall in **Q5**.
Write the acceleration of free fall in the
format $g = \ldots\ldots \pm \ldots\ldots\ m\,s^{-2}$. *(4 marks)*

3.8 Projectile motion

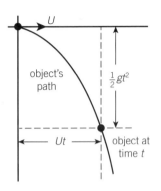

▲ **Figure 1** *An object projected horizontally*

Revision tip

You can use the equations of motion to analyse the *vertical* motion of a projectile. The horizontal velocity of a projectile stays the same.

3.8 Projectile motion

An object thrown vertically on the Earth will describe a straight-line path. An object thrown at an angle to the vertical will follow a curved (parabolic) path. You can analyse the motion of projectiles using the equations of motion.

Independent horizontal and vertical motions

When the effects of air resistance are ignored, all projectiles on the Earth will have an acceleration of $9.81\,\mathrm{m\,s^{-2}}$ vertically downwards. The component of g in the horizontal direction is zero because $g\cos 90° = 0$. Therefore

- Horizontally: The horizontal velocity remains constant.
- Vertically: The velocity changes and the motion can be described using the equations of motion.

Figure 1 shows the path described by an object projected horizontally with an initial velocity equal to U.

Table 1 lists the equations for horizontal and vertical motion.

▼ **Table 1**

	Horizontal motion	Vertical motion
Acceleration	zero	$+g$
Displacement	horizontal displacement $= x$ $x = Ut$	vertical displacement $= y$ initial velocity $= U\cos 90° = 0$ Using $s = ut + \frac{1}{2}at^2 \Rightarrow y = \frac{1}{2}gt^2$
Velocity	U (remains constant)	Using '$v = u + at$' $\Rightarrow v = gt$

 Worked example: Projected horizontally

A metal ball is projected horizontally with a velocity of $3.0\,\mathrm{m\,s^{-1}}$ from the end of a flat table of height 75 cm. Calculate the time it takes before it hits the floor below.

Step 1: Write down the important quantities for the vertical motion of the ball. Assume downward direction is positive.

$s = 0.75\,\mathrm{m}$ $u = 0$ $a = +9.81\,\mathrm{m\,s^{-2}}$ $t = ?$

Step 2: Identify the correct *suvat* equation, rearrange the equation, substitute the values, and calculate a.

$$s = ut + \tfrac{1}{2}at^2 = \tfrac{1}{2}gt^2$$

$$t = \sqrt{\frac{2s}{g}} = \sqrt{\frac{2 \times 0.75}{9.81}} = 0.39\,\mathrm{s}$$

$$t = 0.39\,\mathrm{s}\ (2\,\mathrm{s.f.})$$

Projected at an angle

Figure 2 shows a projectile fired at a velocity v at an angle θ to the horizontal.

You can analyse the motion of this projectile by independently examining the horizontal and vertical motions.

- Horizontally: The velocity remains constant at $v\cos\theta$.
- Vertically: The initial velocity is $v\sin\theta$.

The acceleration is $-g$. (The vertical downward direction is taken as *positive*.)

▲ **Figure 2** *An object projected at an angle to the horizontal*

Worked example: At an angle

A heavy ball is projected at a velocity of 12 m s^{-1} at an angle of $40°$ to the horizontal. Calculate the maximum height of the ball.

Step 1: Write down the important quantities for the vertical motion of the ball.

Note: At the maximum height, the ball stops momentarily in the vertical direction.

$$s = ? \qquad u = 12 \sin 40° \qquad v = 0 \qquad a = -9.81 \text{ m s}^{-2}$$

Step 2: Identify the correct *suvat* equation, rearrange the equation, substitute the values, and calculate *s*.

$$v^2 = u^2 + 2as$$
$$s = \frac{v^2 - u^2}{2a} = \frac{0 - (12\sin 40)^2}{2 \times -9.81}$$
$$s = 3.0 \text{ m (2 s.f.)}$$

Summary questions

1   A ball is projected horizontally at a velocity of 5.0 m s^{-1} from a tall platform.
    State and explain the value of the horizontal velocity.   (*2 marks*)
2   Calculate the horizontal displacement of the ball in **Q1** after 0.25 s.   (*1 mark*)

3   The ball in **Q1** takes 0.70 s before it lands on the ground below.
    Calculate the height of the platform.   (*3 marks*)
4   A bullet is fired from a gun at a horizontal velocity of 250 m s^{-1}.
    Calculate the horizontal and vertical displacements of the bullet after a time of 0.30 s in flight.   (*4 marks*)

5   A golf ball has a velocity of 30 m s^{-1} at an angle of $45°$ to the horizontal ground.
    Calculate its maximum height.   (*3 marks*)
6   For the ball in **Q5**, calculate its horizontal displacement when it lands on the ground.   (*3 marks*)

1 A student plots a graph to determine the distance travelled by an object.

The area of which graph is equal to the distance travelled?

A Force against time.

B Acceleration against time.

C Displacement against time.

D Velocity against time. *(1 mark)*

2 A ball is dropped from rest at time $t = 0$. Air resistance has negligible effect on the motion of the ball.

What is the distance travelled by the ball between $t = 2.0\,\text{s}$ and $t = 3.0\,\text{s}$?

A 4.9 m

B 20 m

C 25 m

D 44 m *(1 mark)*

3 A student conducts an experiment on the acceleration of free fall g.
Her lab book has the following information:

equation: $g = \frac{2s}{t^2}$ %   uncertainty in $s = 3.0\%$ % uncertainty in $t = 1.2\%$

What is the percentage uncertainty in the value for g?

A 0.6%

B 1.8%

C 4.2%

D 5.4% *(1 mark)*

4 **a** Define acceleration. *(1 mark)*

b Figure 1 shows the displacement–time graph plotted by a student for a ball rolling down a ramp.

i Use Figure 1 to describe and explain the motion of the ball. *(2 marks)*

ii Use Figure 1 to determine the velocity of the ball at time $t = 2.0\,\text{s}$. *(3 marks)*

iii The ball was at rest at time $t = 0$.

Use your answer to (ii) to calculate the acceleration of the ball. *(2 marks)*

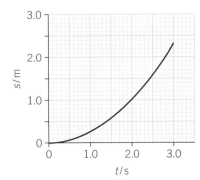

▲ Figure 1

5 A heavy metal ball is dropped from different heights. The time t taken to fall to the ground is recorded for each height h. Figure 2 shows a graph plotted to determine the acceleration of free fall g.

a Explain why plotting h against t^2 produces a straight-line graph through the origin. *(2 marks)*

b Use Figure 2 to determine a value for g. Explain your answer. *(3 marks)*

c State and explain the change, if any, to the graph in Figure 2 when the experiment is conducted with a much heavier metal ball. *(1 mark)*

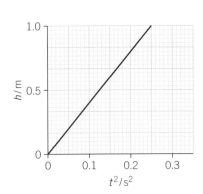

▲ Figure 2

Chapter 4 Forces in action

In this chapter you will learn about ...

- [ ] Mass and weight

- [ ] Centre of mass and centre of gravity

- [ ] Free body diagram

- [ ] Drag and terminal velocity

- [ ] Moment and torque

- [ ] Equilibrium

- [ ] Triangle of forces

- [ ] Density

- [ ] Pressure

- [ ] Archimedes' principle

FORCES IN ACTION
4.1 Force, mass, and weight
4.2 Centre of mass
4.3 Free-body diagrams
Specification reference: 3.2.1, 3.2.3

4.1 Force, mass, and weight

A resultant force F acting on an object of mass m will produce acceleration a. The resultant force, mass, and acceleration are related by the following equation:

$$\text{resultant force} = \text{mass} \times \text{acceleration}$$

or

$$F = ma$$

Force and acceleration are both vectors. The direction of the acceleration is in the same direction as the net force. The SI unit for force is the newton (N).

- For a constant mass, $F \propto a$
- For a constant acceleration, $F \propto m$
- For a constant force, $a \propto \dfrac{1}{m}$

The **newton** is defined as the resultant force that will give a mass of 1 kg an acceleration of $1\,\text{m s}^{-2}$ in the direction of the force.

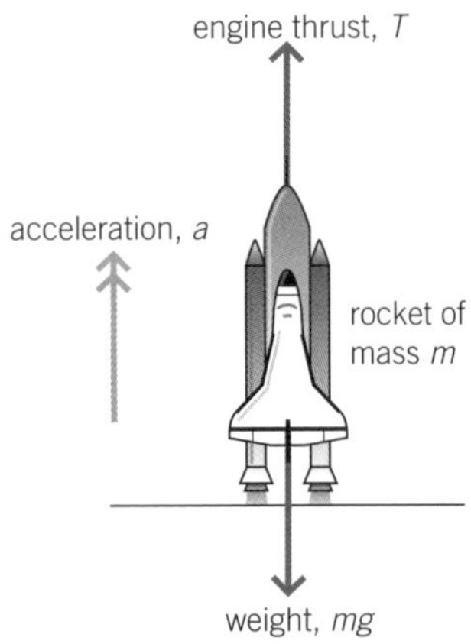

Weight

Mass and weight are not the same.

The **weight** of an object is defined as the gravitational force acting on the object.

An object in free fall on the surface of the Earth has an acceleration g. According to Newton's second law ($F = ma$ above), the weight W of the object must be equal to the product of the mass m of the object and the acceleration of free fall g. Therefore

$$W = mg$$

Figure 1 shows a rocket about to lift off. In order to determine its vertical acceleration, you need to determine the resultant force F on this rocket, where

$$F = \text{thrust} - \text{weight}$$

engine thrust, T

acceleration, a

rocket of mass m

weight, mg

▲ **Figure 1** *What is the resultant force acting on this rocket?*

> **Revision tip**
> In the equation $F = ma$, F is the resultant force acting on the object. When $F = 0$, $a = 0$, the object can either be stationary or travelling at a constant velocity.

4.2 Centre of mass

On the Earth, the centre of gravity and the centre of mass are at the same point. In deep space, where there is no gravitational field, there is no centre of gravity, but the object has a centre of mass.

Centre of gravity is defined as a point where the entire weight of the object appears to act.

Centre of mass is defined as a point through which any externally applied force produces straight-line motion without any rotation.

Experiment to find the centre of gravity

You can determine the centre of gravity of a flat object using the following steps:

1. Suspend the object freely from a point (see Figure 2).
2. Use a plumb-line to draw a straight vertical line on the object.

3. Repeat step 1 using different suspension points.
4. Determine the point of intersection of these straight lines.
5. The intersection point is the centre of gravity.

4.3 Free-body diagram

A free-body diagram shows all the forces acting on a particular object. The following named forces are very useful when drawing free-body diagrams:

thrust   weight   friction   normal contact force

drag   tension   upthrust

Figure 3 shows a block on a ramp and all the forces acting on it.

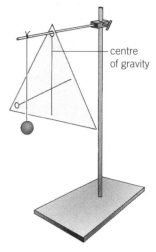

▲ **Figure 2** *Determining centre of gravity*

 Worked example: Block on a ramp

Use the free-body diagram shown in Figure 3 to determine the frictional force *F* and the normal contact force *N*.

Step 1: Always start with a neat free-body diagram – this has already been done for you.

Step 2: The block is stationary therefore the resultant force is zero. Determine *F* by resolving the 1.20 N force along the ramp.

force up the ramp = force down the ramp

$F = 1.20 \cos 60°$ (The angle between the 1.20 N force and the ramp is 60°.)

$F = 0.60\,\text{N}$ (2 s.f.)

Step 3: Determine *N* by resolving the 1.20 N force perpendicularly to the ramp.

$N = 1.20 \cos 30°$

$N = 1.0\,\text{N}$ (2 s.f.)

Synoptic link

The equation $F = ma$ is often referred to as Newton's second law. As you will see in Topic 7.3, Newton's second law of motion, this law is defined in terms of rate of change of momentum. $F = ma$ is just a special case for constant mass.

Summary questions

1 A car of 1000 kg starts from rest. The constant forward force acting on the car is 400 N.
Calculate the initial acceleration of the car. *(1 mark)*
2 After some time, the air resistance acting on the car in **Q1** is 150 N.
Calculate the instantaneous acceleration of the car. *(2 marks)*
3 A car is travelling along a straight level road at a constant velocity. State and explain the resultant force acting on the car. *(2 marks)*
4 A 20 N force acting on an object produces an acceleration of 4.0 m s⁻². Predict its acceleration when the force is 65 N. *(2 marks)*
5 An electron experiences two forces acting at right angles. The magnitude of each force is 2.0×10^{-15} N. The mass of the electron is 9.1×10^{-31} kg. Calculate the acceleration of the electron. *(3 marks)*
6 The electron in **Q5** is initially at rest. Calculate the distance travelled after 20 ns of acceleration. *(2 marks)*

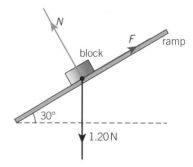

▲ **Figure 3** *Forces acting on a stationary block on a ramp*

4.4 Drag and terminal velocity

An object falling in a vacuum on the Earth will have an acceleration of $9.81\ m\,s^{-2}$ because there is only one force acting on the object – its weight. Objects moving through the air will also experience a resistive force (drag) and an upthrust. The resultant force on the object is no longer its weight and therefore its acceleration cannot be $9.81\ m\,s^{-2}$.

Drag

Resistive forces originate when two materials rub against each other. The term drag is used for the resistive force experienced by an object moving through a fluid (liquid or gas). The factors affecting drag are:

● The speed of the object (the greater the speed, the greater is the drag).

● The cross-sectional area at right angles to the direction of travel (the larger the area, the greater is the drag).

● The type of fluid or its viscosity.

For many objects, drag force is directly proportional to $speed^2$. Table 1 shows how you can test the relationship between drag and speed – the ratio of force to $speed^2$ is a constant.

▼ **Table 1** *Drag is proportional to $speed^2$. A ten-fold increase in the speed of an object will increase the drag by a factor of 10^2 or 100*

speed / $m\,s^{-1}$	2.0	3.0	4.0	5.0	6.0
drag / N	3.2	7.2	12.8	20	28.8
$\dfrac{drag}{speed^2}$ / $N\,s^2\,m^{-2}$	0.80	0.80	0.80	0.80	0.80

Terminal velocity

For a given object of fixed area, the drag will simply depend on the speed of the falling object. Figure 1 shows a skydiver of mass m at three stages in his downward motion through the air.

drag force

drag force

Just before falling ⇒	During the flight ⇒	At terminal velocity ⇒
● speed = 0 ● drag = 0 ● resultant force F = weight ● acceleration = g	● speed > 0 ● drag > 0 ● resultant force $F = mg$ – drag ● acceleration = $\dfrac{mg - drag}{m}$	● speed = constant ● drag = weight ● resultant force = 0 ● acceleration = 0

▲ **Figure 1** *Falling vertically through the air*

At the **terminal velocity**, the speed of the skydiver is constant and his acceleration is zero. The net force on the skydiver is zero therefore drag = weight (if we assume the upthrust to be negligible).

Figure 2 shows the velocity–time graph for an object falling through a fluid. Remember that the gradient of the graph is equal to acceleration. The acceleration is maximum and equal to g at time = 0 and the acceleration is zero at terminal velocity.

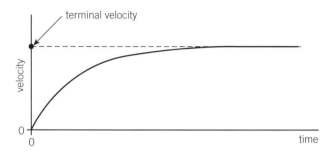

▲ **Figure 2** *Velocity–time graph for an object falling through a fluid*

Investigating drag

Figure 3 shows one possible arrangement for investigating the factors affecting drag.

Revision tip
Do not use the term 'gravity' to mean 'weight'.

▤ Worked example: Drag

A paper cone of mass 5.0 g is dropped from a height of 1.00 m. It reaches terminal velocity almost immediately after release and spends 1.4 s in flight. Calculate the terminal velocity of the cone and the maximum drag.

Step 1: Calculate the terminal velocity v of the paper cone.

$$v = \frac{\text{distance}}{\text{time}} = \frac{1.00}{1.4} = 0.71 \text{ m s}^{-1}$$

Step 2: Use your knowledge of terminal velocity to determine drag.

At terminal velocity, resultant force = 0.

$\text{drag} = \text{weight} = mg$

$\text{drag} = 5.0 \times 10^{-3} \times 9.81 = 4.9 \times 10^{-2} \text{ N (2 s.f.)}$

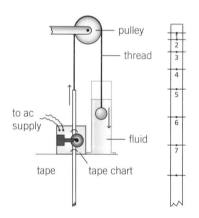

▲ **Figure 3** *The falling object is connected to a tape that passes through a ticker timer. The ticker timer produces 50 dots per second on the moving tape*

Summary questions

1 A small car and a large truck are travelling at the same speed. State and explain which of these will experience a greater drag force.   *(1 mark)*

2 State the resultant force on an object travelling at terminal velocity.   *(1 mark)*

3 A 2.0 kg mass is dropped from rest.
   Calculate the initial resultant force and acceleration of this mass.   *(2 marks)*

4 A skydiver of total mass 70 kg is falling through air.
   The drag force acting on the skydiver is 300 N.
   Calculate the acceleration of the skydiver.   *(3 marks)*

5 Use the data in Table 1 to derive a relationship between drag D and speed v.   *(1 mark)*

6 The results shown in Table 1 are for an object of mass 100 g.
   Predict the terminal velocity of this object when falling through air.   *(3 marks)*

4.5 Moments and equilibrium
4.6 Couples and torques
Specification reference: 3.2.3

4.5 Moments and equilibrium

A body is in equilibrium when the forces acting on the object do not produce any rotation or any acceleration. No acceleration means that the resultant force on the object must be zero. The object can either have a constant velocity or be stationary. As you will see later, the total moment acting on the object must also be zero.

Moment of a force

The 'turning effect' of a force acting on an object is called a moment. A moment is applied to a door about its hinges when you pull the door at its handle.

Moment of a force is defined as the product of the force applied and the perpendicular distance of the line of action of the force from the axis or point of rotation.

Therefore

moment = Fx

where F is the force and x is the perpendicular distance.

A moment can either be clockwise or anticlockwise. The SI unit for moment is N m, but you can also use N cm.

▲ **Figure 1** *Moment of the force is the product of the force F and the perpendicular distance x*

The principle of moments

The two conditions for an object in equilibrium are:

● resultant force = 0

● resultant moment = 0

The second condition is the same as the principle of moments.

Principle of moments: The sum of the clockwise moments about a point or an axis is equal to the sum of the anticlockwise moments about the same point or axis.

Figure 2 shows a uniform beam pivoted at its centre of gravity. It is in equilibrium and balanced horizontally by two weights W_1 and W_2. When taking moments about the pivot, we get

clockwise moment = anticlockwise moment

$$W_2 d_2 = W_1 d_1$$

The force at the pivot must act vertically upwards and equal to $W_1 + W_2$; this is because the net force on the beam must be zero.

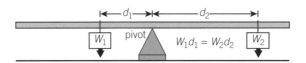

▲ **Figure 2** *A uniform beam in equilibrium*

> **Revision tip**
> For equilibrium, both the net force and net moment acting on the object must be zero.

Worked example: Equilibrium

Figure 3 shows a uniform shelf of weight
28 N held in equilibrium by a cord. Calculate
the tension T in the cord.

Step 1: Determine the perpendicular
distance d of the line of action of T
from the left hand side of the shelf.

$\tan\theta = \dfrac{0.40}{0.60}$ $\theta = \tan^{-1}(0.666...) = 33.7°$

$\sin 33.7° = \dfrac{d}{0.60}$ $d = 0.6 \times \sin 33.7° = 0.33\,\text{m}$

Step 2: Use the principle of moments to
determine T. The centre of gravity of the shelf is at its midpoint – it is 0.30 m
from the end of the shelf.

Take moments about the left hand side of the shelf.

clockwise moment = anticlockwise moment

$28 \times 0.30 = 0.33 \times T$

$T = 25\,\text{N}$ (2 s.f.)

▲ **Figure 3**

4.6 Couples and torques

A couple in physics means two equal but opposite forces acting on an object.
The forces must be parallel and along different lines. See Figure 4.

Torque of a couple

The **torque** of a couple is defined as the product of one of the forces and the
perpendicular separation between the forces.

$$\text{torque} = Fd$$

The torque of a couple is the same as the total moment of the two forces
about their midpoint, c. Torque is also measured in N m.

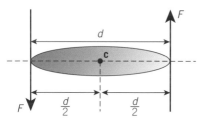

▲ **Figure 4** *A couple gives rise to a torque. The magnitude of the torque is Fd.*

Summary questions

1 A 2.0 N force acts at a perpendicular distance of 10 cm from the pivot.
Calculate the moment of the force. *(1 mark)*
2 The moment of a force is 20 N m. The magnitude of the force
is 400 N. Calculate the perpendicular distance of the force
from the pivot. *(2 marks)*
3 A couple has two 3.0 N forces with a perpendicular separation
of 15 cm.
Calculate the torque of the couple. *(1 mark)*
4 In Figure 2, $W_1 = 1.2$ N, $d_1 = 20$ cm and $W_2 = 0.80$ N. Calculate:
  a the distance d_2 in cm; *(2 marks)*
  b the force at the pivot. *(1 mark)*
5 Figure 5 shows a beam of weight W in equilibrium.
Determine expressions for the vertical contact forces S_x and
S_y in terms of d_x, d_y, and W. *(4 marks)*
6 The beam in Figure 5 has mass 100 N, $d_x = 0.80$ m, and $d_y = 1.20$ m.
Calculate the values of the forces S_x and S_y. *(2 marks)*

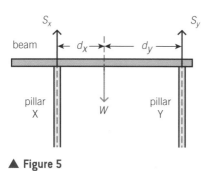

▲ **Figure 5**

4.7 Triangle of forces

For a point object to be in equilibrium the resultant force must be zero. In Topics 2.3, Scalar and vector quantities and 2.4, Adding vectors, you saw the rules for constructing a vector diagram to determine the resultant of two vectors. These rules can be extended to several forces. If an object is in equilibrium under the action of three coplanar (in the same plane) forces, then the vector diagram will form a closed triangle. This triangle is called a triangle of forces, see Figure 1.

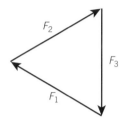

▲ **Figure 1** *Three forces acting on a point object in equilibrium will produce a closed vector triangle or a triangle of forces*

Equilibrium

Figure 2 shows the free-body diagram for a point object subjected to three forces. The object is in equilibrium. The resultant force on the object is zero. You can therefore construct a triangle of forces. Notice that the arrows on this diagram are all in a cyclic order.

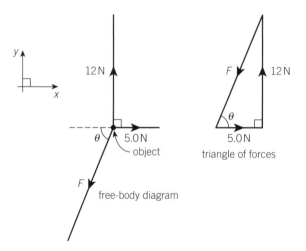

▲ **Figure 2** *A triangle of forces can be constructed from a free-body diagram. Notice that the resultant force of any two forces has a magnitude equal to the third force and has a direction opposite to this third force*

Resolving forces

There is an alternative to drawing a triangle of forces – you can resolve forces. When the resultant force is zero, then the total force in two mutually perpendicular directions must individually also be zero.

For the object in Figure 2 this implies:

In the x-direction the total force = 0 therefore $F\cos\theta = 5.0$

In the y-direction the total force = 0 therefore $F\sin\theta = 12$

Model answers: Triangle of forces

Figure 3 shows fours forces acting on a point object. Calculate the magnitude of the force F.

Answer

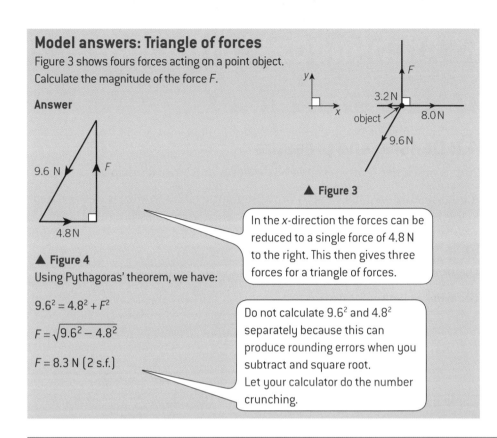

▲ Figure 3

▲ Figure 4

Using Pythagoras' theorem, we have:

$$9.6^2 = 4.8^2 + F^2$$

$$F = \sqrt{9.6^2 - 4.8^2}$$

$$F = 8.3 \text{ N (2 s.f.)}$$

In the x-direction the forces can be reduced to a single force of 4.8 N to the right. This then gives three forces for a triangle of forces.

Do not calculate 9.6^2 and 4.8^2 separately because this can produce rounding errors when you subtract and square root. Let your calculator do the number crunching.

Common misconception

Check the angles carefully and only use the Pythagoras theorem when the triangle of forces has a right angle.

Maths: Sine and cosine rules

Sine rule: $\dfrac{a}{\sin A} = \dfrac{b}{\sin B} = \dfrac{c}{\sin C}$

Cosine rule: $a^2 = b^2 + c^2 - 2bc \cos A$

Summary questions

1 Three coplanar forces act on an object. The object is moving at a constant velocity.
   What is the resultant of these three forces? *(1 mark)*

2 Figure 5 shows the forces S, F, and W acting on a block of wood resting on a ramp.
   Draw a triangle of forces. *(2 marks)*

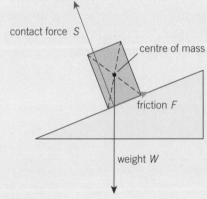

▲ Figure 5

3 Use Figure 2 to determine the magnitude of the force F and the angle θ. *(4 marks)*

4 Use Figure 4 to determine the angle between the 9.6 N force and the x-direction. *(2 marks)*

5 An object of 20 kg is supported by two cables. The angle made by each cable is 20° to the vertical.
   The object is at rest and the tension in each cable is T.
   Use your knowledge of triangle of forces to calculate the magnitude of the tension T. *(3 marks)*

6 Determine the tension T in **Q5** by resolving forces in the vertical direction. *(3 marks)*

4.8 Density and pressure
4.9 $p = h\rho g$ and Archimedes' principle

Specification reference: 3.2.4

4.8 Density and pressure

Lead is much denser than water, but water is much denser than air.

A book resting on a table exerts pressure on the table. This pressure is related to the weight of the book and its cross-sectional area.

Density

The **density** of a substance is defined as its mass per unit volume.

The word equation for density is:

$$\text{density} = \frac{\text{mass}}{\text{volume}}$$

This may be written as

$$\rho = \frac{m}{V}$$

where ρ is the density, m is the mass, and V is the volume. The SI unit for density is $kg\,m^{-3}$.

> **Revision tip**
> $1\,cm^3 = (10^{-2}\,m)^3 = 10^{-6}\,m^3$
>
> $1\,mm^2 = (10^{-3}\,m)^3 = 10^{-9}\,m^3$

Determining density

In order to calculate density, you need to determine the mass of the substance and its volume.

- The mass of a substance can be measured using a top pan balance.
- The volume of a regular solid can be calculated once its dimensions are measured using a ruler, a vernier calliper, or a micrometer. For an irregular solid, its volume can be determined from the volume of water displaced when it is completely submerged. The volume of the displaced water can be measured directly using a measuring cylinder.

Pressure

Pressure is the normal force exerted on a surface per unit cross-sectional area.

The word equation for pressure is:

$$\text{pressure} = \frac{\text{force}}{\text{cross-sectional area}}$$

This may be written as

$$p = \frac{F}{A}$$

where p is the pressure, F is the force, and A is the cross-sectional area. The SI unit for pressure is $N\,m^{-2}$ or pascal (Pa). $1\,Pa = 1\,N\,m^{-2}$.

4.9 $p = h\rho g$ and Archimedes' principle

Imagine swimming under water. You will experience pressure from the water and also an upward force called upthrust.

$$p = h\rho g$$

Figure 1 shows a fluid column of height h and cross-sectional area A. The density of the fluid is ρ.

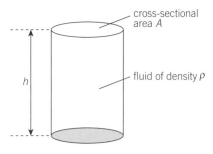

▲ **Figure 1** *A column of fluid exerts pressure at its base*

cross-sectional area A

fluid of density ρ

h

pressure at the base = weight of column/cross-sectional area

$p = \dfrac{mg}{A}$ (weight = mass × g = mg)

$p = \dfrac{(\rho V)g}{A}$ (m = ρ × volume of column = ρV)

$p = \dfrac{V}{A}\rho g$

$p = h\rho g$ (height h of column = V/A)

The pressure p exerted by the column is independent of its cross-sectional area and $p \propto h$.

Archimedes' principle

An object submerged in a fluid (liquid or gas) experiences an upward force – the upthrust, because the pressure at the bottom surface of the object is greater than the pressure at its top surface.

Archimedes' principle: The upthrust exerted on a body immersed in a fluid, whether fully or partially submerged, is equal to the weight of the fluid that the body displaces.

 Worked example: Upthrust

An empty balloon of weight 0.024 N is filled with helium until its volume is $2.0 \times 10^{-2}\,\text{m}^3$. Calculate the net upward force on the balloon when it is released.

density of helium = 0.18 kg m⁻³

density of air = 1.3 kg m⁻³

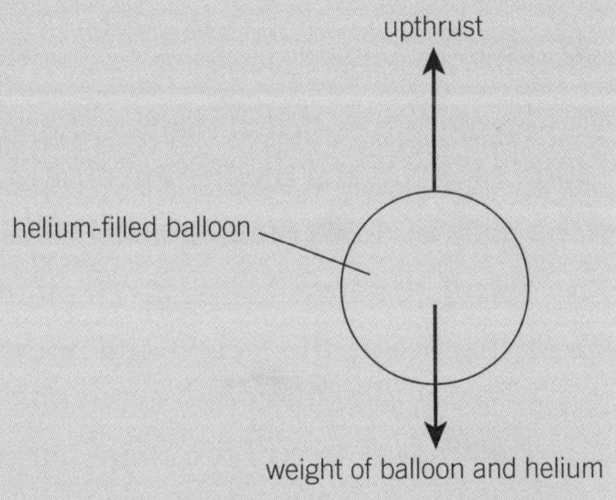

Step 1: Calculate the total downward force on the balloon.

total downward force = weight of balloon + weight of helium

total downward force = 0.024 + (2.0 × 10⁻² × 0.18) × 9.81 = 0.0593 N

Step 2: Use Archimedes' principle to calculate the upthrust and therefore the net force.

upthrust = weight of air displaced = (2.0 × 10⁻² × 1.3) × 9.81 = 0.255 N

net upward force = 0.255 − 0.0593 = 0.20 N (2 s.f.)

▲ **Figure 2** *Forces on the helium-filled balloon*

(labels: upthrust; helium-filled balloon; weight of balloon and helium)

Summary questions

Data required: density of water = 1.0 × 10³ kg m⁻³   *atmospheric pressure = 1.0 × 10⁵ Pa*

1 Calculate the density of a liquid of volume 0.50 m³ and mass 350 kg.   *(1 mark)*
2 Calculate the pressure at the base of a 3.0 × 10⁴ kg concrete column of cross-sectional area of 1.2 m².   *(2 marks)*

3 Calculate the vertical force on a circular surface of radius 15 cm due to the atmosphere.   *(2 marks)*
4 Calculate the total pressure at the bottom of a swimming pool where the depth of water is 3.0 m.   *(3 marks)*

5 The mass of the Earth is 6.0 × 10²⁴ kg and it has a radius of 6.4 Mm. Calculate the average density of the Earth.   *(2 marks)*
6 Mercury is 13.6 times denser than water. Calculate the height of a mercury column that provides at its base a pressure equivalent to atmospheric pressure.   *(2 marks)*

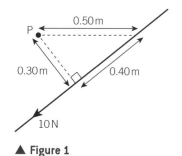
▲ Figure 1

1 Which is the correct definition for the centre of gravity of an object?

The centre of gravity is the point where ...

A the middle of the object happens to be

B all the mass appears to be

C the weight of the objects appears to be

D the net force is zero.   (1 mark)

2 What is the moment of the force about the pivot P in Figure 1?

A 3.0 N

B 4.0 N

C 5.0 N

D 12 N   (1 mark)

3 Which base units are used to measure pressure?

A $kg\,m^{-2}$

B $kg\,m\,s^{-1}$

C $kg\,m^{3}\,s^{-2}$

D $kg\,m^{-1}\,s^{-2}$ (1 mark)

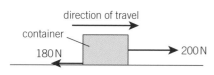
▲ Figure 2

4 A container is pulled along horizontal ground. Figure 2 shows the pulling force of 200 N and the frictional force of 180 N acting on the container.

The mass of the container is 400 kg.

a Calculate its horizontal acceleration.   (2 marks)

b Explain why the weight and normal contact force have no effect on the horizontal acceleration of the container.   (1 mark)

c The surface area of the container is $1.8\,m^{2}$. Calculate the pressure it exerts on the ground.   (2 marks)

5 a State the principle of moments.   (1 mark)

b Figure 3 shows two of the forces acting on a uniform board.

The tension T in the cable is at an angle of 45° to the vertical and the weight of the board is 1800 N.

i The density of the material used to make the board is $900\,kg\,m^{-3}$. Calculate the volume of the board.   (3 marks)

ii Calculate the tension T in the cable.   (3 marks)

iii Explain why the force at **X** must have a component in the horizontal direction.   (1 mark)

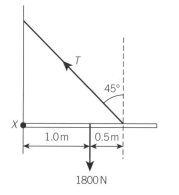
▲ Figure 3

6 A ship is towed at **constant** speed by two tugboats, see Figure 4.

The tension T in each cable attached to the ship is 8.6 kN.

a State and explain the resultant force acting on the ship. (1 mark)

b Calculate the total force due to the tensions in the cables. (3 marks)

c State and explain the direction and magnitude of the drag acting on the ship.   (2 marks)

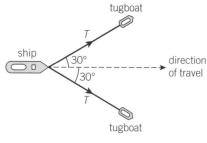
▲ Figure 4

Chapter 5 Work, energy, and power

In this chapter you will learn about ...

- ☐ Work done

- ☐ Energy

- ☐ Conservation of energy

- ☐ Kinetic energy

- ☐ Gravitational potential energy

- ☐ Power

- ☐ Efficiency

5
WORK, ENERGY, AND POWER
5.1 Work done and energy
5.2 Conservation of energy
Specification reference: 3.3.1

5.1 Work done and energy

Work is done when the point of application of a force moves. Work done on an object is linked to energy transfer of the object. A force does no work if there is no motion.

Work done

Work done is defined as the product of force F and the distance x moved in the direction of the force.

The word equation for work done is:

work done = force × distance moved in the direction of the force

The equation for work done is $W = F \times x$

Work done is a scalar quantity. The SI unit for work done is N m or joule (J).
$$1\,J = 1\,Nm.$$

1 **joule** is defined as the work done by a force of 1 N when the point of application of the force moves a distance of 1 m in the direction of the force.

If the force acts at an angle θ to the distance moved (see Figure 1), then the work done by the force is:

work done = component of force in direction of travel × distance moved

$$W = F \cos \theta \times x \qquad \text{or} \qquad W = Fx \cos \theta$$

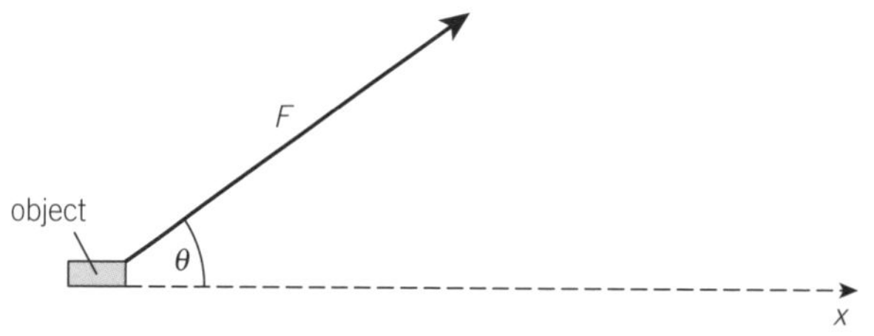

▲ **Figure 1** *Work done is given by the equation W = Fx cos θ*

5.2 Conservation of energy

Energy can take many different forms – kinetic energy, gravitational potential energy, elastic potential energy, thermal (heat) energy, sound energy, and so on. A car moving on a hill possesses both kinetic energy and gravitational potential energy. The chemical energy in the fuel produces lots of thermal energy.

Energy

Energy is the capacity to do work.

The work done on an object is equal to the energy transferred, that is,

work done = energy transferred

This means that 600 J of work done in lifting a crate vertically will increase the gravitational potential energy of the crate by 600 J.

Revision tip
The term 'potential' in physics is used to mean 'stored'.

Principle of conservation of energy

Energy can be converted from one form to another. For example, an object falling through the air on the Earth converts gravitational potential energy to kinetic energy and thermal energy. However, the total energy of the system remains the same.

The principle of **conservation of energy** states that the total energy of a closed system remains constant – energy can never be created or destroyed, but it can be transferred from one form to another.

Revision tip
A closed system is one where there are no external forces acting.

 Worked example: Rough surface

A rope is used to drag a heavy box along a horizontal surface at a constant speed. The tension in the rope is 38 N. The rope makes an angle of 42° to the horizontal. The crate moves a horizontal distance of 15 m. Calculate the work done on the box.

Step 1: Write down the important quantities given in the question.

$F = 38$ N $x = 15$ m $\theta = 42°$

Step 2: Use the equation $W = Fx \cos \theta$ to calculate the work done by the force.

$W = Fx \cos \theta$

$W = 38 \times 15 \times \cos 42° = 420$ N (2 s.f.)

Summary questions

1. An object of weight 20 N falls through a vertical distance of 5.0 m. Calculate the work done by the weight. *(1 mark)*
2. The falling object in **Q1** transfers 30 J of energy to the surrounding air. Determine the kinetic energy of the object after falling 5.0 m. *(1 mark)*

3. A 100 N force acting at an angle of 45° to the horizontal moves an object through a horizontal distance of 20 m. Calculate the work done by the force. *(2 marks)*
4. A ball is rolling along on a smooth horizontal surface at a constant velocity. Explain why no work is done by the weight of the ball. *(2 marks)*

5. A force of 20 N acts on an object. The work done by the force is 100 J. The distance moved by the object is 8.0 m. Calculate the angle between the force and direction of motion of the object. *(2 marks)*
6. A 2.0 kg metal sphere falls through a vertical distance of 10 m. The kinetic energy of the ball just before it hits the ground is 120 J. Calculate the average drag force acting on the falling sphere. *(4 marks)*

5.3 KE and GPE

In mechanics, you need to be familiar with both kinetic energy (KE) and gravitational potential energy (GPE). KE is associated with a moving object and GPE is linked to the position of an object in a gravitational field. GPE is energy 'stored' by an object. In Topic 6.2, you will come across elastic potential energy – energy 'stored' when the shape of an object is changed.

Kinetic energy

The kinetic energy E_k of a moving object is given by the equation

$$E_k = \frac{1}{2}mv^2$$

where m is the mass of the object and v is its speed.

Kinetic energy is a scalar quantity. The base units of kinetic energy are $kg\,m^2\,s^{-2}$, which is the same as joule (J). Kinetic energy of an object is directly proportional to speed^2 – increasing the speed by a factor of 10 will increase its kinetic energy by a factor of $10^2 = 100$.

Common misconception

In the equation $E_k = \frac{1}{2}mv^2$, only the speed v is squared.
A common error made is squaring the term '$\frac{1}{2}mv$'. Just be vigilant.

Maths: Standard form or scientific notation

For an object with initial speed u and final speed v, the change in kinetic energy is $\frac{1}{2}m(v^2 - u^2)$.

This is not the same as $\frac{1}{2}m(v - u)^2$.

Model answer: KE of an accelerating car

A car of mass 900 kg is travelling along at a velocity of 5.0 m s^{-1}. The car accelerates at 3.0 m s^{-2} for 4.0 s. Calculate the change in its kinetic energy in this period of time.

Answer

Final speed:

$u = 5.0\,m\,s^{-1}$ $a = 3.0\,m\,s^{-2}$ $t = 4.0\,s$

$v = u + at = 5.0 + 3.0 \times 4.0 = 17\,m\,s^{-1}$

> You need to calculate the final speed of the car using one of the equations of motion.

Initial KE: $E_k = \frac{1}{2}mv^2 = \frac{1}{2} \times 900 \times 5.0^2$

Final KE: $E_k = \frac{1}{2}mv^2 = \frac{1}{2} \times 900 \times 17^2$

Change in kinetic energy $= \Delta E_k$

$\Delta E_k = \frac{1}{2} \times 900 \times (17^2 - 5.0^2)$

$\Delta E_k = 1.2 \times 10^5\,J$ (2 s.f.)

> You can calculate the individual kinetic energies and then subtract. This can lead to rounding and transfer errors.
>
> It is much neater to do the calculation as a single step on your calculator.

Gravitational potential energy

Figure 1 shows an object of mass m falling through a vertical distance h in a vacuum. The work done by the weight must equal the change in the gravitational potential energy E_p. Therefore

$$E_p = \text{force} \times \text{distance moved in the direction of the weight}$$

$$E_p = (mg) \times h$$

$$E_p = mgh$$

Gravitational potential energy is a scalar quantity. The SI unit is joule (J).

KE and GPE changes

There are many situations where energy is transferred between kinetic energy and gravitational potential energy. Examples include a rollercoaster, a swinging pendulum, and a ball rolling up or down a slope.

In Figure 1, the object is initially at rest and has speed v after falling through the vertical distance h.

According to the principle of conservation of energy, the sum of the KE and GPE of the object at any instant must be constant, as long as there are no thermal losses. This is equivalent to:

change in GPE = change in KE

$$mgh = \frac{1}{2}mv^2$$

The mass m cancels on both sides of the equation. Therefore

$$v^2 = 2gh$$

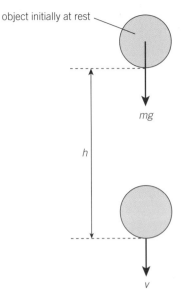

▲ **Figure 1** *The work done by the falling weight is mgh*

Summary questions

1 Calculate the change in the gravitational potential energy of a 1500 kg lift travelling through a vertical distance of 310 m. *(1 mark)*

2 Calculate the kinetic energy of a dust particle of mass 1.0 g travelling at 120 km s^{-1} in deep space. *(2 marks)*

3 A stone falls vertically. The change in its GPE is 20 J.
   Explain the change in the KE of the stone. State any assumption made. *(2 marks)*

4 A 1000 kg car has kinetic energy 50 kJ. Calculate its speed. *(2 marks)*

5 An electron is travelling at a speed of 1.2×10^5 m s^{-1}. Its kinetic energy is increased by 8.0×10^{-21} J.
   The mass of an electron is 9.1×10^{-31} kg. Calculate its final speed. *(4 marks)*

6 Figure 2 shows a simple pendulum. The object is released from rest from a height of h_0.
   At a height h it has speed v.

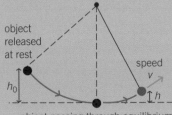

▲ **Figure 2**

   a Describe the energy changes taking place as the object travels from its maximum height to the height h. *(2 marks)*

   b Calculate v given $h_0 = 3.0$ m and $h = 0.20h_0$. *(4 marks)*

5.4 Power and efficiency

The term power is the most frequently misused term in physics examinations. Though linked to energy or work done, power has a precise definition, so you must use it carefully. The efficiency of a device or a mechanical system cannot be greater than 100%. If you get an answer greater than 100% in a calculation, then you have definitely gone wrong and need to double-check your working.

Power

Power is defined as the rate of work done or the rate of energy transfer.

The word equation for power is

$$\text{power} = \frac{\text{work done}}{\text{time}} \qquad \text{or} \qquad \text{power} = \frac{\text{energy transfer}}{\text{time}}$$

This may be written as

$$P = \frac{W}{t}$$

where P is the power, W is the work done (or energy transfer), and t is the time taken. The SI unit for power is J s^{-1} or watt (W).

1 **watt** is defined as 1 joule of work done per second.

The equation above may also be written as $W = Pt$

A 24 W table lamp will transfer 24 J of energy per second. In 2 s, the energy transfer is 24 × 2 = 48 J, and so on.

Maths: Rate

The term 'rate' in physics means 'per unit time' or simply 'divided by time'. So rate of work done can be written as $\dfrac{\text{work done}}{\text{time}}$

Common misconception

The letter W is used for work done (or energy transfer). It must not be confused with W (watt), which is the unit for power.

 ### Worked example: Car power

A 1000 kg electric car, starting from rest, can reach a top speed of 30 m s^{-1} in 4.5 s. Calculate the average output power of the car in kW.

Step 1: Calculate the change in the kinetic energy of the car.

$$E_k = \frac{1}{2}mv^2 = \frac{1}{2} \times 1000 \times 30^2 = 4.5 \times 10^5 \, \text{J}$$

Step 2: Use the equation for power to calculate the average output power of the car in watts.

$$P = \text{energy transfer/time}$$

$$P = \frac{4.5 \times 10^5}{4.5}$$

$$P = 1.0 \times 10^5 \, \text{W}$$

Step 3: Convert the power from W to kW using 1 kW = 10^3 W.

$$\text{power} = \frac{1.0 \times 10^5}{10^3} = 100 \, \text{kW} \, (2 \, \text{s.f.})$$

Power and motion

Consider a car travelling at a constant speed v on a level road. The constant speed means that the car has zero acceleration and the net force on the car must be equal to zero. The forward force F acting on the car must be equal to the total resistive force, see Figure 1. In this situation all the work done by the force F is transferred not to the kinetic energy of the car, but to thermal losses.

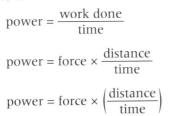

direction of travel (speed = v)

▲ **Figure 1** *The output power of the car is given by the equation P = Fv*

The output power P of the car can be determined as follows:

$$\text{power} = \frac{\text{work done}}{\text{time}}$$

$$\text{power} = \text{force} \times \frac{\text{distance}}{\text{time}}$$

$$\text{power} = \text{force} \times \left(\frac{\text{distance}}{\text{time}}\right)$$

or

$$P = Fv$$

where v is the speed of the car.

Efficiency

The efficiency of a system or a device is defined by the following equations:

$$\text{efficiency} = \frac{\text{useful output energy}}{\text{total input energy}} \times 100\%$$

or

$$\text{efficiency} = \frac{\text{useful output power}}{\text{total input power}} \times 100\%$$

It is important to remember the following:

- Efficiency can be expressed either as a percentage or as a number between 0 and 1.0.
- The efficiency of a system cannot exceed 100% because this would violate the principle of conservation of energy.
- The efficiency of most mechanical systems is less than 100% because of thermal losses caused by frictional losses.

Summary questions

1   The total input energy to a motor is 56 J and the useful output energy is 2.4 J.
    Calculate the efficiency of the motor.   *(1 mark)*

2   The input power to a table lamp is 24 W.
    Calculate the input energy to the lamp in a period of 1.0 hour.   *(2 marks)*

3   The output power of a car is 6.0 kW. The car is travelling on a level road at a constant speed of 20 m s⁻¹.
    Calculate the forward force acting on the car.   *(2 marks)*

4   The useful output power to a device is 20 W. The efficiency of the device is 0.25.
    Calculate the total input power to the device.   *(2 marks)*

5   A motor can lift a 100 g mass through a height of 120 cm in a time of 2.4 s.
    a   Calculate the output power of the motor.   *(3 marks)*
    b   The motor has an efficiency of 12%. Calculate the input power to the motor.   *(2 marks)*

6   The drag force acting on a car is directly proportional to speed².
    The speed of the car is doubled.
    Calculate the factor by which the output power of the car would increase.   *(3 marks)*

1   Which is the correct unit for power?

    A Js

    B Js^{-1}

    C Nm

    D Nm^{-1} *(1 mark)*

2   The mass of a truck is doubled and its speed is also doubled.

    What is the factor by which its kinetic energy increases?

    A 2

    B 4

    C 8

    D 16   *(1 mark)*

3   A load of mass 40 kg is lifted vertically at a constant speed of 1.5 m s^{-1}.

    What is the rate of work done in lifting the load?

    A 45 W

    B 60 W

    C 440 W

    D 590 W   *(1 mark)*

4   A pendulum bob is released from rest from a vertical height *h*. The speed of the bob at the bottom of the swing is *v*.

    What is the correct equation for *v* and *h*?

    A $v = gh$

    B $v = 2gh$

    C $v^2 = 2gh$

    D $v^2 = gh$ *(1 mark)*

5   **a** State the principle of conservation of energy.   *(1 mark)*

    b A metal ball of mass 0.040 kg is dropped into a viscous liquid. After travelling a vertical distance of 0.080 m the ball has a velocity of 0.90 m s^{-1}. Calculate:

        i   the loss in the gravitational potential energy of the ball;   *(1 mark)*

        ii the kinetic energy of the ball;   *(1 mark)*

        iii the average work done against drag;   *(2 marks)*

        iv the average value for drag.   *(2 marks)*

6   Figure 1 shows a trolley of mass 0.80 kg being pulled along a horizontal table by a falling object of mass 0.21 kg.

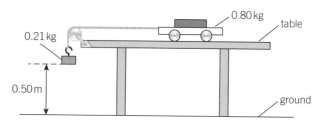

▲ **Figure 1**

    The trolley is held at rest. The string attached to the trolley is taut. The 0.21 kg mass is 0.50 m above the ground.

    a Show that the acceleration of the trolley is about 2 m s^{-2}.   *(2 marks)*

    b Calculate the kinetic energy of the trolley just before the 0.21 kg mass hits the ground.   *(3 marks)*

    c Calculate the change in the gravitational potential energy of the 0.21 kg mass.   *(1 mark)*

    d Explain why the answers in (b) and (c) are not the same.   *(1 mark)*

Chapter 6 Materials

In this chapter you will learn about ...

- ☐ Hooke's law

- ☐ Force constant

- ☐ Elastic potential energy

- ☐ Force–extension graphs

- ☐ Stress and strain

- ☐ Elastic and plastic behaviour

- ☐ Stress-strain graphs

- ☐ The Young modulus

6

MATERIALS
6.1 Springs and Hooke's law
6.2 Elastic potential energy
Specification reference: 3.4.1, 3.4.2

6.1 Springs and Hooke's law

A spring or a wire can be stretched by a pair of equal and opposite forces; such forces are called tensile forces. Forces that squash a spring or an object are called compressive forces. Hooke's law can be used to model the behaviour of springs and wires.

Hooke's law

Hooke's law: The extension of the spring is directly proportional to the force applied. This is true as long as the elastic limit of the spring is not exceeded.

The extension x is the difference between the final length of the spring and its original length.

Force constant

Figure 1 shows the force against extension graph for a spring (or a wire).

- The spring shows elastic behaviour up to point A (elastic limit).
  - **Elastic:** Removal of the force will return the spring to its original length.
- The spring obeys Hooke's law in the linear region of the graph.

$$F \propto x$$

or

$$F = kx$$

In the equation above, k is a constant for the spring known as the force constant. The SI unit for force constant is $N\,m^{-1}$.

- The gradient of the linear section of the graph is equal to force constant.
- Beyond the elastic limit the spring shows plastic behaviour.
  - **Plastic:** Removal of the force will not return the spring to its original length – it will have a permanent deformation.

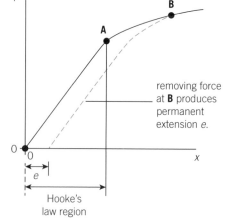

▲ **Figure 1** *Force F against extension x graph for a spring*

Revision tip
Stiffer springs have larger values of force constant.

6.2 Elastic potential energy

Energy is stored in a spring when it is extended or compressed elastically. This stored energy is called elastic potential energy.

Elastic potential energy equations

The area under a force–extension graph is equal to the work done by the force, see Figure 2.

For a spring (or wire) with extension x and force F, the work done on the spring is equal to the elastic potential energy E.

E = area of the triangle of 'height' F and 'base length' x

$$E = \frac{1}{2}Fx$$

Since $F = kx$, we also have

$$E = \frac{1}{2}(kx)x = \frac{1}{2}kx^2$$

For a given spring, $E \propto x^2$; doubling the extension will quadruple the energy stored by the spring.

▲ **Figure 2** *The area under a straight-line force–extension graph is equal to elastic potential energy, E*

Worked example: Energy stored in a spring

A compressible spring of force constant 60 N m^{-1} has its compression changed from 10.0 cm to 18.0 cm. Calculate the change in the energy stored in the spring.

Step 1: Write down the quantities given in the question.

$k = 60$ N m^{-1} $\quad x_1 = 0.100$ m $\quad x_2 = 0.180$ m

Step 2: Use the equation $E = \frac{1}{2}kx^2$ to calculate the change in the energy stored.

initial stored energy $= \frac{1}{2} \times 60 \times 0.100^2$

final stored energy $= \frac{1}{2} \times 60 \times 0.180^2$

change in stored energy $= \frac{1}{2} \times 60 \times [0.180^2 - 0.100^2]$

change in stored energy $= 0.67$ J (2 s.f.)

Common misconception

The work done by a constant force is given by the equation $W = Fx$, but for a spring or wire, the work done (or the elastic potential energy) is given by $E = \frac{1}{2}Fx$.

Summary questions

1 An object of weight 1.2 N is hung from the bottom of a spring. The spring has a force constant of 25 N m^{-1}.
   Calculate the extension of the spring. *(2 marks)*

2 A student records the following results from an experiment on a wire.
   force = 10 N and extension = 2.5 mm
   force = 30 N and extension = 9.2 mm
   Discuss whether or not the wire obeys Hooke's law. *(3 marks)*

3 A spring has force constant 120 N m^{-1}.
   Calculate the elastic potential energy in the spring when it has extension 20 mm. *(2 marks)*

4 The energy stored in the spring in **Q3** is 5.4 J for a new extension.
   Calculate this new extension. *(3 marks)*

5 The extension of a spring is increased by a factor of 5.
   Calculate the factor by which the elastic potential energy of the spring would increase. *(2 marks)*

6 A spring is used to propel a small metal ball of mass 20 g.
   The spring has force constant 150 N m^{-1} and its maximum compression is 9.0 cm.
   Calculate the maximum speed of the metal ball. *(4 marks)*

6.3 Deforming materials
6.4 Stress, strain, and the Young modulus

6.3 Deforming materials

Not all materials deform in the same way. A ductile material can be drawn into a wire and it stretches a lot beyond its elastic limit. Metals such as gold and copper are both ductile. A brittle material snaps when it reaches its elastic limit. Glass and cast iron are both brittle. A polymeric material such as rubber deforms elastically.

Loading and unloading

Figure 1 shows the force–extension graphs for a metal wire, rubber, and polythene.

- **Metal wire:** For forces less than the elastic limit, the wire obeys Hooke's law and it behaves elastically. It deforms plastically for forces greater than the elastic limit.
- **Rubber:** Rubber has long chains of molecules. It behaves elastically and does not obey Hooke's law.
- **Polythene:** Polythene does not obey Hooke's law and it undergoes plastic deformation for very small values of force.

6.4 Stress, strain, and the Young modulus

The factors that affect the extension x of a wire are: its original length L, its cross-sectional area A, the force F applied to the wire and the material of the wire.

Stress and strain

Tensile stress is defined as the force per unit cross-sectional area.

The word equation for stress σ is

$$\text{stress} = \frac{\text{force}}{\text{cross-sectional area}} \quad \text{or} \quad \sigma = \frac{F}{A}$$

The unit of stress is the same as that for pressure: N m^{-2} or pascal (Pa).

Tensile strain is defined as the extension (or compression) per unit original length.

The word equation for strain ε is

$$\text{strain} = \frac{\text{extension}}{\text{original length}} \quad \text{or} \quad \varepsilon = \frac{x}{L}$$

Strain has no unit. However, sometimes it is written as a percentage. For example, a strain of 0.012 may also be written as 1.2%.

Young modulus

Figure 2 shows the stress–strain graph for a ductile material.

When the material does not exceed its elastic limit,

$$\text{stress} \propto \text{strain}$$

or

$$E = \frac{\sigma}{\varepsilon}$$

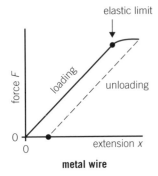

metal wire

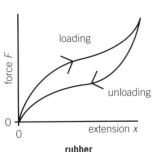

rubber

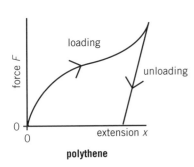

polythene

▲ **Figure 1** *Force–extension graphs*

Breaking stress is the value of the stress at which the material snaps or breaks.

The **ultimate tensile strength** is the maximum stress the material can withstand.

▲ **Figure 2** *Stress–strain graph for a ductile material*

where E is the Young modulus of a material. The unit for Young modulus is $N\,m^{-2}$ or Pa.

Young modulus of a material is defined as the ratio of stress to strain.

Stress–strain graphs

The force–extension and stress–strain graphs have the same shapes for rubber and polythene.

The stress–strain graph for a brittle material is the same as Figure 2, except there is no plastic deformation.

Determining Young modulus

To determine the Young modulus of a material in the form of a long wire:

- Plot a graph of stress against strain. The Young modulus is the gradient of the straight-line section of the graph.

- Each value of stress is determined by hanging a mass m from the end of the wire and measuring the diameter d of the wire using a micrometer.

$$\text{stress} = \sigma = \frac{mg}{\left(\frac{\pi d^2}{4}\right)}$$

- Each value of strain is determined by measuring the extension x and the original length L using a metre rule. To improve the accuracy and precision, the extension should be measured using a device with a vernier scale ($\pm 0.1\,mm$ or better).

 Worked example: Force constant and the Young modulus

Show that the force constant k of a wire is equal to $\frac{EA}{L}$, where E is the Young modulus, A is the cross-sectional area of the wire, and L is the original length of the wire.

Step 1: Write the equations for stress, strain, and the Young modulus.

$$\text{stress} = \sigma = \frac{F}{A} \qquad \text{strain} = \varepsilon = \frac{x}{L} \qquad \text{Young modulus} = E = \frac{\sigma}{\varepsilon}$$

Step 2: Substitute the stress and strain labels into the equation for Young modulus.

$$E = \frac{\sigma}{\varepsilon} = \frac{\left(\frac{F}{A}\right)}{\left(\frac{x}{L}\right)} = \frac{FL}{Ax}$$

Step 3: Rearrange the equation with F being the subject.

$$F = \frac{EA}{L}x$$

Comparing the equation above with $F = kx$, the force constant k must be $\frac{EA}{L}$

Summary questions

1 State the units of stress, strain, and Young modulus. (1 mark)

2 A rubber band of original length 10.0 cm is extended to a length of 15.0 cm. Calculate the strain. (2 marks)

3 A 12 N weight is hung from a wire of radius 1.0 mm. Calculate the stress in the wire. (2 marks)

4 The material of the wire in **Q3** has Young modulus 1.8×10^{11} Pa. Calculate the strain of the wire. (3 marks)

5 Use the results recorded by a student to calculate the Young modulus of the material.
mass supported by wire = 5.0 kg   original length = 3.2 m
extension of wire = 3.0 mm   diameter of wire = 1.4 mm (4 marks)

6 For the wire in **Q5**, calculate the energy stored in the wire per unit volume. (3 marks)

Chapter 6 Practice questions

1 Which of these is the correct unit for the force constant of a spring?

    A J s

    B J s^{-1}

    C N m

    D N m^{-1} *(1 mark)*

2 Which of these statements is correct?
Rubber is elastic because...

    A it obeys Hooke's law

    B it has no plastic deformation

    C it does not return all the energy stored

    D it returns to its original shape when forces are removed.   *(1 mark)*

3 The extension of a spring is x and the energy stored (elastic potential energy) is E. The spring is pulled until its new extension is $3x$.

What is the *change* in the energy stored in the spring if its extension is altered from x to $3x$?

    A $2E$

    B $3E$

    C $8E$

    D $9E$ *(1 mark)*

4 A 1.5 kg load is suspended from the end of a wire of diameter 1.2 mm.

What is the tensile stress of this wire?

    A 3.9×10^{3} Pa

    B 1.2×10^{4} Pa

    C 3.3×10^{6} Pa

    D 1.3×0^{7} Pa   *(1 mark)*

5 **a** Figure 1 show the force F against extension x graph for a spring.

    i Calculate the force constant of the spring.   *(2 marks)*

    ii Calculate the extension of the spring when the applied force is 9.0 N.

        State any assumption made.   *(3 marks)*

  b Two identical springs are connected in series and support a load of weight 10 N. The force constant of each spring is 40 N m^{-1}. Calculate the total energy stored in the springs.   *(3 marks)*

6 **a** Define the Young modulus of a material.   *(1 mark)*

  b Figure 2 shows the stress against strain graph for a metal in the form of a wire being investigated by a student.

    The material breaks at point B when the applied force is 16 N.

    i Calculate the cross-sectional area of the wire when it breaks.   *(2 marks)*

    ii Calculate the Young modulus of the metal.   *(3 marks)*

    iii State and explain how the shape of the graph would change when a thicker wire of the same metal is investigated.   *(2 marks)*

7 A metal wire of length 1.20 m is fixed at its top end and an object is hung from its lower end. The extension of the wire is 0.54 mm. The cross-sectional area of the wire is 2.1×10^{-7} m^2 and the Young modulus of the wire is 8.0×10^{10} Pa.

  a Calculate the strain of the wire.   *(2 marks)*

  b Calculate the mass of the object hung from the wire.   *(4 marks)*

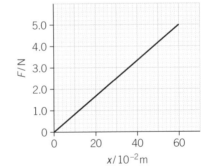

▲ Figure 1

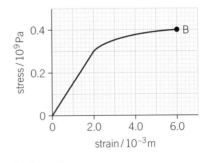

▲ Figure 2

Chapter 7 Laws of motion and momentum

In this chapter you will learn about ...

☐ Newton's first, second, and third laws

☐ Momentum

☐ Rate of change of momentum

☐ Impulse

☐ Force–time graph

☐ Conservation of momentum

☐ Elastic collision

☐ Inelastic collision

7 LAWS OF MOTION AND MOMENTUM
7.1 Newton's first and third laws of motion
7.2 Linear momentum

Specification reference: 3.1.2, 3.5.1, 3.5.2

7.1 Newton's first and third laws of motion

Newton's laws are universal laws that can be used to model the motion of planets and gas atoms. It is important to understand these laws.

First law

Newton's first law of motion: An object will remain at rest or continue to move with constant velocity unless acted upon by a resultant force.

When the resultant force on an object is zero, it will either be motionless or travel at a constant velocity. A non-zero resultant force will accelerate the object.

Third law

Newton's third law of motion: When two objects interact, they exert equal and opposite forces on each other.

This is one of the most misunderstood laws. It is worth noting the following points:

- The forces cannot act on a single object.
- The forces are in opposite directions.
- The forces have the same magnitude.
- Both forces must be of the same type (e.g., gravitational, electrostatic, etc.).

All interactions can be explained in terms of four fundamental forces – gravitational, electromagnetic, strong nuclear, and weak nuclear.

7.2 Linear momentum

Knowledge of momentum is essential in Newton's second law (see Topic 7.3) and collisions. Momentum is a vector quantity. In one dimension, we can use positive and negative signs to denote the directions.

Momentum

The **linear momentum** p, or just momentum, is defined as the product of the mass m of an object and its velocity v.

$$momentum = mass \times velocity$$

or

$$p = mv$$

The SI unit of momentum is $kg\,m\,s^{-1}$.

Common misconception

Momentum is defined as the product of mass (a scalar) and velocity (a vector).
A common mistake made in exams is to define it as: momentum = mass × speed.
This must be avoided.

Conservation of momentum

For a system of interacting objects, the total momentum in a specified direction remains constant, as long as no external forces act on the system.

In a closed system, where no external forces act, the total initial momentum is equal to the total final momentum. It is important to take account of the vector nature of velocity and momentum when using this law.

- In all collisions, the total energy and the total momentum remain constant.
- In a perfectly elastic collision the total kinetic energy remains constant.
- In an inelastic collision there is a change in the kinetic energy, with transformation of energy to other forms (e.g., heat, sound, etc.).

🖩 Worked example: Explosive

An explosive is used to break up a stationary large rock. After the explosion the rock breaks up into two fragments. The mass of the smaller fragment is 30% of the total mass of the rock. The immediate velocity of the larger fragment is $15 \, \text{m s}^{-1}$. Calculate the ratio:

$$\frac{\text{kinetic energy of smaller fragment}}{\text{kinetic energy of larger fragment}}$$

Step 1: Use the principle of conservation of momentum to determine the velocity of the smaller fragment.

The initial momentum is zero – therefore, the final momentum must also be zero.

final momentum = initial momentum

$$(0.30 \, M \times v) + (0.70 \, M \times 15) = 0 \qquad M = \text{total mass of the rock}$$

$$v = \frac{0.70 \, M \times 15}{0.30 \, M} = -35 \, \text{m s}^{-1}$$

The minus sign signifies the fragments flying off in opposite directions. The speed of the smaller fragment is $35 \, \text{m s}^{-1}$.

Step 2: Calculate the ratio of kinetic energies.

$$\text{ratio} = \frac{\frac{1}{2} \times 0.30 \, M \times 35^2}{\frac{1}{2} \times 0.70 \, M \times 15^2} = 2.3 \, (2 \, \text{s.f.})$$

Revision tip

Momentum is a vector quantity and therefore can be resolved.

Summary questions

1. State and explain the gravitational force exerted by a person of weight 700 N on the Earth. *(1 mark)*
2. Calculate the momentum of a 900 kg car travelling at a speed of $30 \, \text{m s}^{-1}$. *(1 mark)*
3. Calculate the momentum of a 1.2 kg object dropped from rest after falling for 3.0 s. *(3 marks)*
4. A cannon of mass 1200 kg fires a 20 kg shell at a speed of $240 \, \text{m s}^{-1}$. Calculate the magnitude of the recoil velocity of the cannon. *(3 marks)*
5. Figure 1 shows a ball of mass m before and after hitting a wall. Calculate the change in momentum of the ball. *(2 marks)*
6. A 1100 kg car is travelling at $30 \, \text{m s}^{-1}$. The momentum of the car decreases by $1.3 \times 10^4 \, \text{kg m s}^{-1}$. Calculate the final speed of the car. *(3 marks)*
7. A 40 g metal ball travelling at $80 \, \text{m s}^{-1}$ hits a stationary lump of clay of mass 300 g. The ball becomes embedded in the clay. Calculate:
   a. the common speed of the clay and metal ball immediately after the impact; *(3 marks)*
   b. the loss in kinetic energy. *(2 marks)*

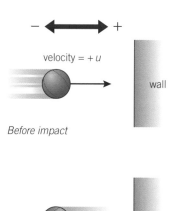

Before impact

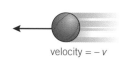

After impact

▲ Figure 1

7.3 Newton's second law of motion
7.4 Impulse
7.5 Collisions in two dimensions

Specification reference: 3.5.1, 3.5.2

7.3 Newton's second law of motion

You have already met the equation $F = ma$; this is a special case of Newton's second law of motion. This law relates the rate of change of momentum of an object to the resultant force acting on the object.

It is important that you do not state this law as $F = ma$.

Newton's second law

Newton's second law: The net (resultant) force acting on an object is directly proportional to the rate of change of its momentum, and is in the same direction.

resultant force $\propto$ rate of change of momentum
or
resultant force = $k \times$ rate of change of momentum.

In SI units, the constant k is taken as equal to 1, so this law can be written as
resultant force = rate of change of momentum

$$F = \frac{\Delta p}{\Delta t}$$

where F is the resultant force and Δp is the change in momentum in a time Δt.

Units: $F \to (\text{N})$ $\Delta p \to (\text{kg m s}^{-1})$ $\Delta t \to (\text{s})$

$F = ma$

The equation $F = ma$ can be derived from Newton's second law.

For an object of constant mass m with initial velocity u and final velocity v after a time t, the resultant force F is given by

$$F = \frac{\Delta p}{\Delta t} = \frac{mv - mu}{t} = m\left(\frac{v - u}{t}\right) = ma$$

A constant force will produce a constant acceleration a.

7.4 Impulse

Impulse of a force is defined as the product of force and time.

According to Newton's second law, the change in momentum Δp of an object is given by $\Delta p = F \times \Delta t$.

Therefore

- change in momentum = impulse

Force–time graph

For a constant force F acting for a time t, the impulse is equal to Ft. This is the same as the area under the force–time graph, see Figure 1. Therefore

- area under force–time graph = impulse = change in momentum

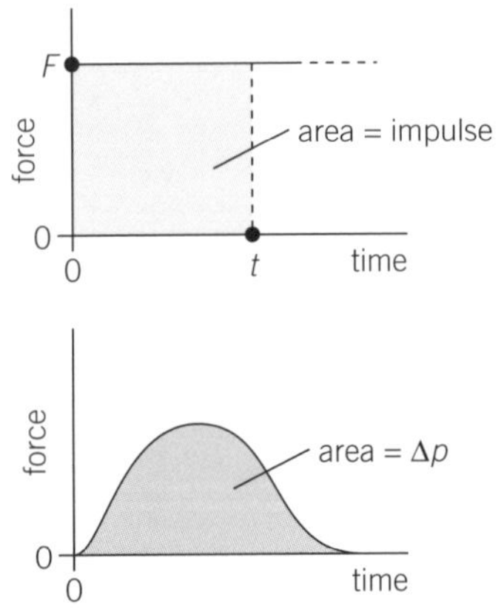

▲ **Figure 1** *The area under a force–time graph is equal to impulse*

Revision tip

Momentum has the same unit as impulse; kg m s^{-1} or N s.

Worked example: *F–t* graph

Figure 2 shows a force *F* against time *t* graph for an object. The change in momentum of the object is 2.0 kg m s⁻¹ in the first 1.0 ms.

Use the graph to determine the total change in momentum of the object.

Step 1: Determine the total area under the graph.

$$\text{total area under the graph} = (4 \times 1) + \left(\frac{1}{2} \times 4 \times 3\right) = 10 \text{ 'units'}$$

Step 2: Determine the change in momentum.

area under graph = impulse = change in momentum

An area of 4 'units' is equal to 2.0 kg m s⁻¹.

Therefore, total change in momentum $= \frac{10}{4} \times 2.0 = 5.0$ kg m s⁻¹ (2 s.f.)

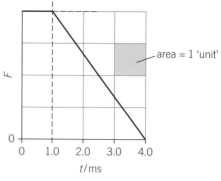
▲ **Figure 2**

7.5 Collisions in two dimensions

For collisions in two dimensions:

● total momentum in the *x*-direction remains constant

● total momentum in the *y*-direction remains constant.

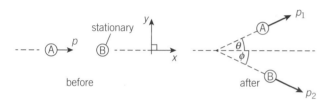

▲ **Figure 3** *There is no change in the total momentum*

Figure 3 shows the collision between objects A and B.

x-direction: initial momentum = final momentum

$$p = p_1 \cos \theta + p_2 \cos \phi$$

y-direction: total momentum is zero

$$p_1 \sin \theta = p_2 \sin \phi$$

Summary questions

1 The change in momentum of a toy car is 0.12 kg m s⁻¹. What is the impulse acting on the toy car? *(1 mark)*

2 The velocity of a 900 kg mass car changes from 30 m s⁻¹ to 10 m s⁻¹ in 5.0 s.
Use the change in momentum of the car to calculate the magnitude of the force acting on the car. *(3 marks)*

3 Figure 4 shows the force–time graph for a car of mass 1000 kg.
Calculate the impulse acting on the car. *(2 marks)*

4 Calculate the change in the velocity of the car in **Q3**. *(2 marks)*

5 A metal ball of mass 40 g hits a solid floor with a speed of 30 m s⁻¹. It rebounds with the same speed. It is in contact with the floor for 2.0 ms.
Calculate the impulse of the force acting on the ball during its impact with the floor. *(3 marks)*

6 Draw a labelled vector diagram for Figure 3 to show that momentum is conserved.
Explain your answer. *(3 marks)*

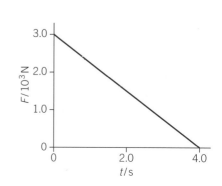
▲ **Figure 4**

Chapter 7 Practice questions

1   What is the area under a force against time graph equal to?

   A energy   **C** acceleration

   B impulse   **D** velocity   *(1 mark)*

2   What quantity is conserved in all collisions?

   A impulse   **C** kinetic energy

   B force   **D** momentum   *(1 mark)*

3   An object is travelling to the right with a momentum of $20\,kg\,m\,s^{-1}$. It collides head-on with another object moving to the left with a momentum of $30\,kg\,m\,s^{-1}$. The objects join together during the collision.

   What is the final momentum of the objects?

   A $10\,kg\,m\,s^{-1}$ to the left   **C** $50\,kg\,m\,s^{-1}$ to the left

   B $10\,kg\,m\,s^{-1}$ to the right   **D** $50\,kg\,m\,s^{-1}$ to the right   *(1 mark)*

4   The momentum of a car is $2000\,kg\,m\,s^{-1}$. The speed of the car increases when a force of $200\,N$ acts on the car for a period of $3.0\,s$.

   What is the final momentum of the car?

   A $600\,kg\,m\,s^{-1}$ **C** $2000\,kg\,m\,s^{-1}$

   B $1400\,kg\,m\,s^{-1}$ **D** $2600\,kg\,m\,s^{-1}$ *(1 mark)*

5   **a** Define linear momentum.   *(1 mark)*

   b State Newton's second law of motion.   *(1 mark)*

   c An object of mass $800\,g$ falls vertically and hits the ground with a speed of $6.0\,m\,s^{-1}$. It rebounds with a speed of $4.0\,m\,s^{-1}$. The contact time with the ground is $25\,ms$.

     i Calculate the change in the momentum of the object.   *(1 mark)*

     ii Calculate the magnitude of the average force exerted by the ground on the object.   *(2 marks)*

     iii State and explain the direction of the force experienced by the ground.   *(2 marks)*

6   **a** Define impulse of a force.   *(1 mark)*

   b Figure 1 shows the variation of the force F experienced by a ball with time t.

     The mass of the ball is $200\,g$. The ball was travelling at a constant initial speed of $3.0\,m\,s^{-1}$ before the force shown in Figure 1 was applied.

     i Describe and explain how the acceleration of the ball varies between $t = 0$ and $t = 0.4\,s$.   *(2 marks)*

     ii Calculate the final speed v of the ball. Explain your answer. *(4 marks)*

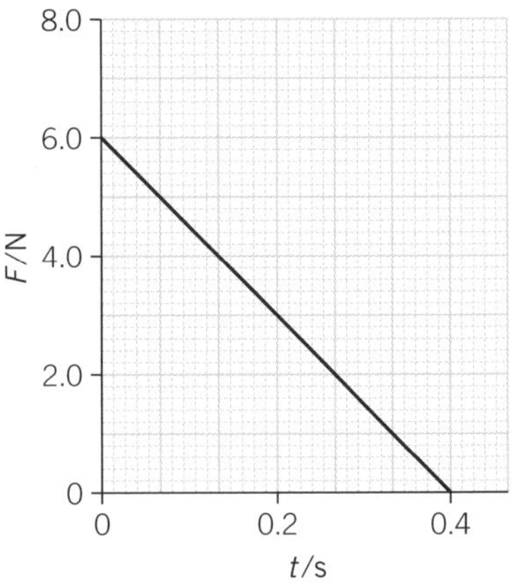

7   **a** Explain what is meant by an inelastic collision.   *(1 mark)*

   b A railway engine of mass $8.0 \times 10^4\,kg$ travelling at a constant speed of $0.50\,m\,s^{-1}$ collides with a stationary carriage of mass $4.0 \times 10^4\,kg$. The engine and the carriage couple together and move off at a constant speed v.

     i Calculate the initial momentum of the engine.   *(1 mark)*

     ii Calculate the speed v. Explain your answer.   *(3 marks)*

     iii Calculate the change in the kinetic energy of:

        1 the engine;   *(2 marks)*

        2 the carriage.   *(1 mark)*

     iv Explain why the answers to (iii)1 and (iii)2 are not the same. *(1 mark)*

▲ Figure 1

Module 4 Electrons, waves, and photons

Chapter 8 Charge and current

In this chapter you will learn about ...

- ☐ Charge
- ☐ Quantisation of charge
- ☐ Charge carriers
- ☐ Current
- ☐ Conventional current
- ☐ Kirchhoff's first law
- ☐ Mean drift velocity
- ☐ Number density
- ☐ Insulators, metals, and semiconductors

8 CHARGE AND CURRENT
8.1 Current and charge
8.2 Moving charges

Specification reference: 4.1.1

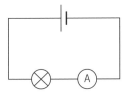

▲ **Figure 1** *The ammeter is connected in series to the lamp*

8.1 Current and charge

Charged particles can either be positive or negative. Charge is measured in coulomb (C). An electron has a negative charge and a proton has a positive charge. In a conducting liquid (an electrolyte) there are negative and positive ions.

An electric current is the flow of charged particles. Current is measured in ampere (A). The ampere is one of the SI base units. In the laboratory you can measure the current in a component using an ammeter connected in series with the component, see Figure 1.

Electric current

Electric current is defined as the rate of flow of charge.

Electric current I can be calculated using the equation

$$I = \frac{\Delta Q}{\Delta t}$$

where ΔQ is the charge transferred in a time Δt.

Units: $I \rightarrow A$ $\quad \Delta Q \rightarrow C$ $\quad \Delta t \rightarrow s$

A current of 1 ampere is the same as a charge of 1 coulomb transferred per second; $1\,A = 1\,C\,s^{-1}$.

A charge of 1 **coulomb** is defined as the flow of charge in a time of 1 second when the current is 1 ampere.

> **Revision tip**
>
> Tiny currents are measured in pA, nA, µA, and mA.
>
> $1\,pA = 10^{-12}\,A$ $\quad 1\,nA = 10^{-9}\,A$
> $1\,\mu A = 10^{-6}\,A$ $\quad 1\,mA = 10^{-3}\,A$

> **Worked example: Tiny current**
>
> The current in a resistor is 3.2 pA. Calculate the number of electrons travelling through the resistor in a time of 1.0 minutes.
>
> **Step 1:** Write down the quantities given in the question.
>
> $I = 3.2 \times 10^{-12}\,A$ $\quad \Delta t = 60\,s$ $\quad \Delta Q = ?$
>
> **Step 2:** Calculate the charge flow ΔQ.
>
> $I = \frac{\Delta Q}{\Delta t}$
>
> $\Delta Q = I\Delta t = 3.2 \times 10^{-12} \times 60$
>
> $\Delta Q = 1.92 \times 10^{-10}\,C$
>
> **Step 3:** The magnitude of the charge on each electron is $1.60 \times 10^{-19}\,C$. Use this to calculate the number of electrons responsible for the charge.
>
> number of electrons $= \frac{1.92 \times 10^{-10}}{1.60 \times 10^{-19}} = 1.2 \times 10^{9}$ (2 s.f.)
>
> The number of electrons passing through the resistor is 1.2 billion.

Quantisation of charge

All objects can be charged by removing or depositing electrons. The magnitude of the charge on a single electron is given the letter e. At a microscopic level, a single electron removed from a neutral atom will give the remaining atom (ion) a positive charge of $+e$, removing two electrons will result in a positive ion of charge of $+2e$, and so on. Adding electrons to a neutral atom can result in a negative ion of charge $-e$, $-2e$, and so on.

- The charge Q on particles is quantised, with $Q = \pm ne$ (n = integer).

8.2 Moving charges

In a metal, the current is due to the movement of electrons. In an electrolyte, the current is due to the simultaneous movement of positive and negative ions.

Electrons and ions

Figure 2 shows the negative electrons in a metal wire moving away from the negative side of the cell. The convention for the direction of current in a circuit is opposite in direction to the flow of electrons.

- The direction of conventional current I is from positive to negative.
- The direction of flow of electrons is from negative to positive.

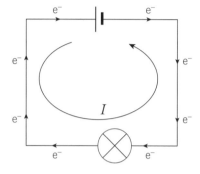

▲ **Figure 2** *The direction of conventional current I is in the opposite direction to the flow of electrons*

Summary questions

1 Name the charged particles responsible for current in a metal wire and in an electrolyte. *(1 mark)*

2 a According to a student the charge of an ion can be $+8.0 \times 10^{-20}$ C. Explain whether or not the student is correct. *(1 mark)*

  b Calculate the current in a diode given that the charge flow is 12 C in a time of 60 s. *(2 marks)*

3 An oil droplet has an excess of 8 electrons. Calculate the charge on the oil droplet. *(2 marks)*

4 A solar cell delivers an average current of 20 mA in a period of 4.0 hours.
  Calculate the total flow of charge through the solar cell. *(2 marks)*

5 Calculate the total number of electrons flowing through the solar cell in **Q4**. *(2 hours)*

6 Modern electronic circuits can measure tiny current equivalent to a million electrons per minute.
  Calculate this tiny current. *(2 hours)*

8.3 Kirchhoff's first law
8.4 Mean drift velocity
Specification reference: 4.1.1, 4.1.2

8.3 Kirchhoff's first law

In an electrical circuit, the charge carriers responsible for electric current are the electrons. Unlike the positive ions, which are fixed, electrons are free to move within a circuit. In a series circuit, you would expect all the electrons entering a particular component to come out. This is because charge cannot be created or destroyed – it is conserved.

The first law

Kirchhoff's first law states that for any point (junction) in an electrical circuit, the sum of currents into that point (junction) is equal to the sum of currents out of that point.

This can be written as

$$\Sigma I_{in} = \Sigma I_{out}$$

where sum ΣI_{in} is the sum of the currents into a point and ΣI_{out} is the sum of the currents out of the same point. Kirchhoff's first law is a natural consequence of the conservation of charge.

Figure 1 shows some examples of Kirchhoff's first law.

Maths: Sum of

The Greek letter sigma Σ is used as a shorthand for 'sum of...'.

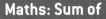
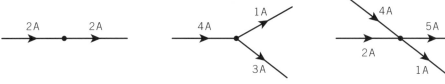

▲ **Figure 1** *Examples of the first law*

Revision tip
The current in a series circuit is constant because of conservation of charge.

8.4 Mean drift velocity

The electrons in a metal move around at high speeds and make frequent collisions with the vibrating fixed positive metal ions. The net result is that the electrons move in random directions. When the wire is connected to a battery or a power supply, the electrons gain an additional velocity towards the positive electrode of the external supply. The mean drift velocity v is the average velocity gained by the electrons along the length of the wire.

Figure 2 shows a cross-section through a current-carrying wire.

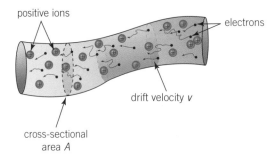

positive ions

electrons

drift velocity v

cross-sectional area A

▲ **Figure 2** *Electrons have a mean drift velocity along the length of the wire because they make repeated collisions with the vibrating positive ions*

I = Anev

The **number density** is the number of charge carriers (e.g. electrons) per unit volume of the material.

We can classify the conduction properties of materials by their number density.

- Metals are good conductor with n about $10^{28}\,\text{m}^{-3}$.
- Insulators such as plastic have much smaller number density than metals.
- Semiconductors such as silicon have a number density between insulators and metals, about $10^{18}\,\text{m}^{-3}$.

The mean drift velocity v depends on the current I in the wire, the cross-sectional area A of the wire, the number density n of the free electrons, and the elementary charge e.

The equation for the current is $I = Anev$.

 Worked example: Lamp filament

The current in a tungsten filament lamp is 0.33 A. The filament has a radius of $2.4 \times 10^{-4}\,\text{m}$. The mean drift velocity of the electrons is $3.0 \times 10^{-4}\,\text{m s}^{-1}$.

Calculate the number density of the free electrons for tungsten.

Step 1: Write down the quantities given in the question.

$$I = 0.33\,\text{A} \quad r = 2.4 \times 10^{-4}\,\text{m} \quad v = 3.0 \times 10^{-4}\,\text{m s}^{-1} \quad e = 1.6 \times 10^{-19}\,\text{C} \quad n = ?$$

Step 2: Rearrange the equation $I = Anev$, substitute the values, and calculate n.

$$n = \frac{I}{Aev} = \frac{0.33}{[\pi \times (2.4 \times 10^{-4})^2] \times 1.6 \times 10^{-19} \times 3.0 \times 10^{-4}}$$

$$n = 3.8 \times 10^{28}\,\text{m}^{-3}\ (2\ \text{s.f.})$$

Summary questions

1 In an electric circuit, 2 billion electrons enter a point. State and explain how many electrons will leave the same point. *(1 mark)*

2 Determine the currents in the part of the circuit shown in Figure 3. *(3 marks)*

3 The mean drift velocity in a resistor is 2.0 mm s^{-1} when the current is 4.0 A.
Calculate the mean drift velocity when the current is reduced to 1.0 A. *(2 marks)*

4 Figure 4 shows a cross-section through a current-carrying conductor. Describe and explain how the mean drift velocity of the free electrons changes from B to A. *(2 marks)*

5 The number density of free electrons for copper is $8.5 \times 10^{28}\,\text{m}^{-3}$. Estimate the number of free electrons in a copper wire of length 1.0 cm and diameter 1.0 mm. *(2 marks)*

6 The number density of free electrons in a metal is $5.0 \times 10^{28}\,\text{m}^{-3}$. Calculate the mean drift velocity of the electrons in a metal wire of cross-sectional area 1.0 mm^2 when the current is 3.0 μA. *(3 marks)*

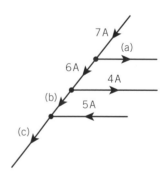

▲ Figure 3

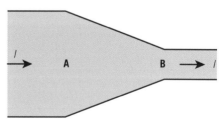

▲ Figure 4

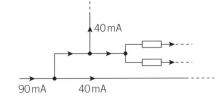

▲ **Figure 1**

1 Which quantity is conserved according to Kirchhoff's first law?

A energy

B charge

C potential difference

D electromotive force (*1 mark*)

2 Figure 1 shows parts of an electrical circuit.
What is the current in one of the identical resistors?

A 5 mA   C 20 mA

B 10 mA   D 40 mA (*1 mark*)

3 How many electrons represent a charge of −6.4 μC?

A 4.0×10^7 C 4.0×10^{13}

B 4.0×10^{10} D 4.0×10^{16} (*1 mark*)

4 The diameter of a current-carrying wire gets thinner in the direction of electron flow.
Which statement is correct about the mean drift velocity of the charge carriers in the direction of electron flow?
The mean drift velocity ...

A decreases

B increases

C stays the same

D is equal to $3 \times 10^8 \, \mathrm{m\,s^{-1}}$. (*1 mark*)

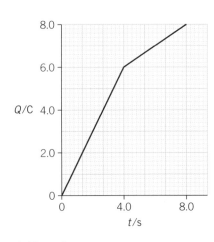

▲ **Figure 2**

5 a Figure 2 shows the conduction of ions within a liquid.
State and explain the direction of the conventional current in the liquid. (*1 mark*)

  b The current in a wire is 40 mA. Calculate:

    i the total charge passing through a point in the wire in a period of 30 s; (*2 marks*)

    ii the total number of electrons responsible for the charge in (i). (*2 marks*)

6 A metal wire of diameter 1.2 mm is connected to an electrical appliance. The current in the wire is 9.5 A and the appliance is operated for a time of 2.0 minutes. The metal has 8.5×10^{22} free electrons per cm³ of the wire. Calculate:

  a the number density n of the free electrons within the wire in m⁻³; (*1 mark*)

  b the mean drift velocity of the electrons; (*3 marks*)

  c the mean distance travelled along the length of the wire by each electron in 2.0 minutes. (*1 mark*)

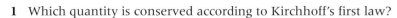

▲ **Figure 3**

7 Figure 3 shows variation of charge Q passing though a point in a circuit with time t.

  a State and explain what physical quantity is equal to the gradient of the graph. (*1 mark*)

  b Calculate the current at time $t = 3.0$ s. (*1 mark*)

  c Describe the variation of current I with time t. (*3 marks*)

Chapter 9 Energy, power, and resistance

In this chapter you will learn about ...

- ☐ Circuit symbols
- ☐ Potential difference (p.d.)
- ☐ Electromotive force (e.m.f.)
- ☐ The electron gun
- ☐ Resistance
- ☐ $I-V$ characteristics
- ☐ Resistors and filament lamps
- ☐ Diodes and light-emitting diodes
- ☐ Resistivity
- ☐ Thermistor and light-dependent resistors (LDR)
- ☐ Electrical power
- ☐ Kilowatt-hour

9 ENERGY, POWER, AND RESISTANCE
9.1 Circuit symbols
9.2 Potential difference and electromotive force
9.3 The electron gun
Specification reference: 4.2.1, 4.2.2

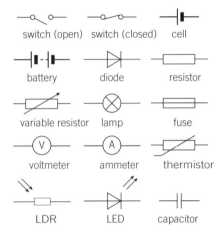

▲ **Figure 1** *Circuit symbols*

9.1 Circuit symbols

Figure 1 shows the circuit symbols used in electrical circuits – use them with great care when drawing circuit diagrams.

9.2 Potential difference and electromotive force

When analysing circuits, it is important that you distinguish the terms potential difference (p.d.) and electromotive force (e.m.f.). A voltmeter is a device calibrated to measure the p.d. across a component – a voltmeter is placed in parallel with the component.

Potential difference

The term potential difference is used when the charge carriers (electrons) lose energy in a component.

Potential difference is defined as the energy transferred from electrical energy to other forms (heat, light, etc.) per unit charge.

The word equation for p.d. V is

$$\text{p.d.} = \frac{\text{energy transferred}}{\text{charge}} \quad \text{or} \quad V = \frac{W}{Q}$$

where W is the energy transferred and Q is the charge flow.

Electromotive force

The term electromotive force is used when charge carriers (electrons) gain energy from a source. A chemical cell, a dynamo, a solar cell, a thermocouple, and a power supply are all examples of sources of e.m.f.

Electromotive force is defined as the energy transferred from chemical energy (or another form) to electrical energy per unit charge.

The word equation for e.m.f. ε is

$$\text{e.m.f.} = \frac{\text{energy transferred}}{\text{charge}} \quad \text{or} \quad \varepsilon = \frac{W}{Q}$$

where W is the energy transferred and Q is the charge flow.

- p.d. and e.m.f. are both measured in volts (V).
- 1 volt = 1 joule per coulomb ($1\,\text{V} = 1\,\text{J}\,\text{C}^{-1}$).
- A potential difference of 1 **volt** is defined as 1 joule of energy transferred per unit coulomb.

> **Revision tip**
> The term 'voltage' is often used instead of potential difference.

> **Revision tip**
> $1\,\text{V} = 1\,\text{J}\,\text{C}^{-1}$
> Think of a voltmeter as an instrument calibrated to show 'joules per coulomb'.

Analysing a circuit

Figure 2 shows a simple electrical circuit. A battery of e.m.f. 3.0 V is connected in series with a filament lamp and a resistor. The p.d. across the lamp is 2.4 V and the p.d. across the resistor is 0.6 V.

- Battery: 3.0 J of chemical energy is transferred into electrical energy per unit coulomb of charge.
- Lamp: 2.4 J of electrical energy is transferred to thermal energy and radiant energy per unit coulomb of charge.
- Resistor: 0.6 J of electrical energy is transferred to thermal energy per unit coulomb of charge.

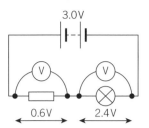

3.0 V

0.6 V   2.4 V

▲ **Figure 2** *Imagine what happens to the energy of 1 C of charge travelling from the battery, around the circuit, and then back to the battery*

9.3 The electron gun

Figure 3 shows an electron gun – a device used to accelerate electrons to high speeds.

The p.d. between the hot filament and the anode is V. The electrons have negligible kinetic energy at the filament.

work done on an electron = final kinetic energy of an electron

$$Ve = \frac{1}{2}mv^2$$

where e is the elementary charge, m is the mass of the electron, and v is the final speed of the electron.

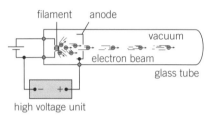

filament   anode

vacuum

electron beam

glass tube

high voltage unit

▲ **Figure 3** *An electron gun*

🖩 Worked example: High-speed electrons

An electron gun produces a beam of electrons of speed $2.0 \times 10^6 \, \text{m s}^{-1}$.

Calculate the accelerating p.d. V.

Step 1: Select the equation relating p.d. and the speed of the electron.

$$Ve = \frac{1}{2}mv^2$$

Step 2: Rearrange to make V the subject.

$$V = \frac{mv^2}{2e}$$

Step 3: Substitute the values and calculate V.

$$V = \frac{9.11 \times 10^{-31} \times (2.0 \times 10^6)^2}{2 \times 1.60 \times 10^{-19}}$$

$$V = 11.4 \, \text{V} \approx 11 \, \text{V} \; (2 \, \text{s.f.})$$

Summary questions

1 Name two sources of e.m.f. *(1 mark)*

2 Calculate the potential difference across a resistor that transfers 20 J of energy when a charge of 4.0 C flows through it. *(2 marks)*

3 A charge of 60 C travels through a power supply of e.m.f. 100 V. Calculate the energy transferred. *(2 marks)*

4 Calculate the energy transferred by an electron travelling through a p.d. of 1.0 kV. *(2 marks)*

5 The current in a filament lamp is 0.25 A and the p.d. across it is 6.0 V. The lamp is operated for 30 s. Calculate the rate of energy transfer in the lamp. *(3 marks)*

6 Calculate the speed of protons accelerated from rest through a potential difference of 10 kV. *(3 marks)*

9.4 Resistance
9.5 *I–V* characteristics
9.6 Diodes

Specification reference: 4.2.3

9.4 Resistance

The term resistance has a precise meaning in physics. You can use a multimeter set on 'ohms' to directly measure the resistance of some components (e.g., resistor, thermistor, etc.).

Defining resistance

The **resistance** of a component in a circuit is defined by the following word equation:

$$\text{resistance} = \frac{\text{potential difference across component}}{\text{current in the component}}$$

or

$$R = \frac{V}{I}$$

where R is the resistance, V is the potential difference, and I is the current. The SI unit for resistance is ohm, Ω.

Units: $V \rightarrow V$ $I \rightarrow A$ $R \rightarrow \Omega$

A resistance of 1 **ohm** is defined as 1 volt per unit ampere.

Determining resistance

Figure 1 shows a circuit that may be used to determine the resistance R of any component. The voltmeter measures the p.d. V across the component and the ammeter measure the current I in the component. The resistance is calculated using the equation $R = \dfrac{V}{I}$

Ohm's law: For a metallic conductor kept at a constant temperature, the current in the wire is directly proportional to the p.d. across its ends.

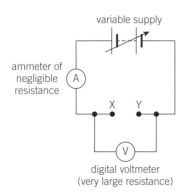

variable supply

ammeter of negligible resistance

X   Y

digital voltmeter (very large resistance)

▲ **Figure 1** *The component is connected between X and Y*

9.5 *I–V* characteristics

The *I–V* characteristic of a component is a graph of current against p.d.

Resistor and filament lamp

Figure 2 shows the *I–V* characteristics of a resistor (a) and a filament lamp (b).

Resistor:

- $I \propto V$ therefore its resistance remains constant.
- A resistor is an ohmic component.

Filament lamp:

- The resistance of the lamp is not constant – the *I–V* graph is not a straight line through the origin.
- The resistance of a filament lamp increases as the current, or the p.d., increases. At a microscopic level, the metal ions of the filament vibrate more quickly and with increased amplitudes. The conducting electrons makes more frequent collisions with these vibrating ions and transfer greater amounts of energy to these ions.
- A filament lamp is a non-ohmic component.

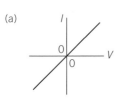

(a)

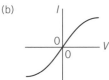

(b)

▲ **Figure 2** *I–V characteristics*

9.6 Diodes

Diodes are components made from semiconductors that conduct in one direction. A light-emitting diode emits light of a specific colour when it conducts. See Figure 3.

▲ **Figure 3** *Symbols for a diode and LED*

Light-emitting diodes

Figure 4 shows the *I–V* characteristics of an ordinary diode (e.g., silicon) and a light-emitting diode, LED.

- The diode does not conduct when it is reverse biased.
- The resistance is infinite for negative p.d.s.
- The diode starts to conduct when it is forward biased and the p.d. is greater than the threshold p.d. V_c.
- The resistance of the diode decreases significantly as the p.d. is increased beyond V_c. This is because of the increase in the number density of the charge carriers.

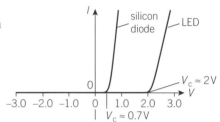

▲ **Figure 4** *I–V characteristics of diodes*

🖩 Worked example: What is it?

A student is investigating a component and records the results below.

Identify the component.

I / A	−20 mA	52 mA
V / V	−1.2 V	4.7 V

Step 1: Eliminate the diode.

The component cannot be a diode because it conducts in 'both directions'.

Step 2: Calculate the resistance at each p.d.

negative values: $R = \dfrac{V}{I} = \dfrac{1.2}{0.02} = 60\,\Omega$ (2 s.f.)

positive values: $R = \dfrac{V}{I} = \dfrac{4.7}{0.052} = 90\,\Omega$ (2 s.f.)

Step 3: Identify the component from the resistance values.

The resistance is not constant, so it cannot be a resistor.

The resistance increases as the p.d. increases, so it must be a filament lamp.

Summary questions

1 Name one non-ohmic component. *(1 mark)*
2 Calculate the p.d. across a 120 Ω resistor with a current of 30 mA. *(1 mark)*

3 The current in a resistor is doubled.
   State and explain what happens to the resistance of the resistor. *(1 mark)*
4 Show that the resistance of a reverse biased diode is infinite. *(1 mark)*

5 The resistance of an LED decreases from 200 Ω to 20 Ω when the p.d. across it is increased from 1.9 V to 2.1 V. Calculate the change in current in the LED. *(3 marks)*
6 For the LED in **Q5**, calculate the percentage change in the number density of the charge carriers. *(2 marks)*

9.7 Resistance and resistivity
9.8 The thermistor
9.9 The LDR

Specification reference: 4.2.3, 4.2.4

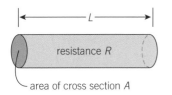

▲ **Figure 1** *Factors affecting resistance*

Revision tip

Resistance and resistivity are very different.

Resistivity is a property of a *material*, whereas resistance depends on the *physical dimensions* of the material.

9.7 Resistance and resistivity

The resistance R of a conductor depends on:

- its length L
- its cross-sectional area A
- its temperature
- the material of the conductor.

Resistivity equation

Figure 1 shows a conductor of length L and cross-sectional area A. For a given temperature, $R \propto L$ and $R \propto \frac{1}{A}$. Therefore:

$$R \propto \frac{L}{A}$$

or

$$R = \frac{\rho L}{A}$$

where ρ is a constant for the material known as its **resistivity**. The SI unit for resistivity is $\Omega\,m$. Metals have much smaller values of resistivity compared with insulators – metals have a greater number density of free electrons. For example: $\rho_{silver} = 1.6 \times 10^{-8}\,\Omega\,m$ and $\rho_{glass} \approx 10^{12}\,\Omega\,m$.

Resistivity and temperature

Metals: Increasing the temperature of a metal increases the frequency and amplitude of vibration of the fixed metal ions. Therefore, the conducting electrons collide more frequently with the vibrating ions and this subsequently leads to greater resistance. The temperature of a metal has almost negligible effect on the number density of the electrons.

Semiconductors: Temperature affects the number density of charge carriers in a semiconductor. The number density increases with temperature and this leads to a dramatic decrease in resistance of the semiconductor.

 Worked example: Very long

A student decides to make a '100 Ω resistor' from a length of manganin wire of cross-sectional area 0.70 mm². The resistivity of manganin is $4.8 \times 10^{-7}\,\Omega\,m$.

Calculate the length of the wire and suggest if the student's idea is feasible.

Step 1: Write down all the quantities given and convert the area into m². $(1\,mm^2 = 10^{-6}\,m^2)$

$R = 100\,\Omega$ $\rho = 4.8 \times 10^{-7}\,\Omega\,m$ $A = 0.70 \times 10^{-6}\,m^2$ $L = ?$

Step 2: Use the resistivity equation to calculate the length.

$$L = \frac{RA}{\rho} = \frac{100 \times 0.70 \times 10^{-6}}{4.8 \times 10^{-7}} = 146\,m \text{ (3 s.f.)}$$

Step 3: Make a suitable comment.

A resistor, about 150 m long, is just not practical in circuits.

The resistor can be made from a material of higher resistivity.

9.8 The thermistor

The resistance of a thermistor depends on its temperature.

Symbol: 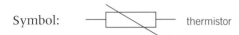 thermistor

Properties of a thermistor

For an NTC thermistor, its resistance decreases as temperature increases. NTC stands for 'negative temperature coefficient', which means the resistance drops as temperature rises.

Figure 2 shows the variation in resistance of a typical thermistor with temperature.

9.9 The LDR

The resistance of an LDR depends on the intensity of the incident light.

Symbol:  LDR

Properties of a light-dependent resistor (LDR)

For an LDR, its resistance decreases as intensity of light incident on it increases. Figure 3 shows the variation of resistance of an LDR with light intensity.

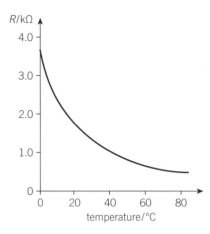
▲ **Figure 2** *Resistance–temperature graph for an NTC thermistor*

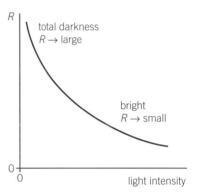
▲ **Figure 3** *Resistance–intensity graph for an LDR*

Summary questions

*Data: resistivity of aluminium = 2.7 × 10⁻⁸ Ω m
resistivity of silver = 1.6 × 10⁻⁸ Ω m*

1 The resistance of a length of wire is 2.3 Ω.
   Calculate the resistance of a similar wire that is 4 times
   longer. (*2 marks*)
2 Calculate the resistance of a cube of aluminium across its opposite
   ends when all the sides are 1.0 m. (*2 marks*)

3 Calculate the resistance of a 1.00 m long silver wire of
   cross-sectional area 1.2 × 10⁻⁶ m². (*2 marks*)
4 Calculate the resistance of an aluminium cable of radius
   1.0 cm and 1.0 km long. (*3 marks*)

5 Use Figure 2 and the temperature ranges 0 °C to 20 °C and
   20 °C to 40 °C to show the effect temperature has on the
   resistance of the thermistor. (*3 marks*)
6 A wire has resistance 12 Ω. It is pulled until its length is 10 times longer.
   Calculate its resistance now. State any assumption made. (*3 marks*)

Revision tip

For both thermistors and LDRs, the resistance decreases because of an increase in the number of charge carriers.

9.10 Electrical energy and power
9.11 Paying for electricity

Specification reference: 4.2.5

9.10 Electrical energy and power

A current-carrying component will transfer electrical energy into other forms. A resistor will transfer energy into thermal energy; whereas an LED will predominantly transfer energy into light. The term power is used to show how quickly this energy is transferred.

Electrical energy

Power is the rate of energy transfer.

For a current-carrying component, the power P is given by the equation

$$P = VI$$

where V is the p.d. across the component and I is the current in the component. The SI unit for power is Js^{-1} or watt (W). Therefore, $1\,W = 1\,Js^{-1}$.

The energy W transferred by a component is the product of power P and the time t. Therefore

$$W = VIt$$

In a period of 1 hour (3600 s), a 240 V lamp with a current of 0.25 A will transfer 216 kJ of electrical energy into heat and light. (Check this for yourself.)

Synoptic link

You have already met power in Topic 5.4, Power and efficiency.

Revision tip

$1\,W = 1\,Js^{-1}$
A power of 20 W just means $20\,Js^{-1}$.

Common misconception

Do not confuse the unit watt (W) with the quantity work done (energy transfer) W – both are represented by the same letter.

Other equations for power

For a resistor, its constant resistance R is given by the equation $R = \frac{V}{I}$. Substituting for V and I into the power equation $P = VI$ gives two more useful equations

$$P = VI = (IR) \times I \qquad \therefore P = I^2R$$

and

$$P = VI = V \times \left(\frac{V}{R}\right) \qquad \therefore P = \frac{V^2}{R}$$

Worked example: Maximum current

A 12 Ω resistor can safely dissipate 0.50 W. Calculate the maximum current in mA for this resistor.

Step 1: Write down the quantities given in the question.

$$R = 12\,\Omega \qquad P = 0.50\,W \qquad I = ?$$

Step 2: Select the correct power equation, rearrange the equation, substitute values, and calculate the current in ampere (A)

$$P = I^2R$$

$$I = \sqrt{\frac{P}{R}} = \sqrt{\frac{0.50}{12}} = 0.20\,A \,(2\text{ s.f.})$$

Step 3: Change the current to mA. (1000 mA = 1 A)

$$\text{current} = 0.20 \times 1000 = 200\,mA \,(2\text{ s.f.})$$

9.11 Paying for electricity

The joule (J) is the SI unit for energy. When considering energy used in domestic and industrial situations, the unit joule is too small. Electricity companies use the kilowatt-hour (kWh) as a convenient unit for billing customers.

Kilowatt-hour

The **kilowatt-hour** (kWh) is defined as the energy transferred by a device with a power of 1 kW operating for a time of 1 hour.

The amount of energy in kWh is calculated as follows

$$\text{number of kWh} = \text{power in kW} \times \text{time in hours}$$

The cost of operating a device is calculated as follows

$$\text{cost} = \text{number of kWh} \times \text{cost per kWh}$$

> **Revision tip**
>
> The kilowatt-hour is an alternative unit for **energy**.
>
> 1 kWh = 3.6 MJ

 Worked example: Charging your phone

A 6.0 W phone charger is used on average for 3.0 hours every day. Calculate the annual cost of using the charger. Assume the cost of each kWh is 8.1p.

Step 1: Calculate the total energy in kWh.

number of kWh for 1 day = 0.006 kW × 3.0 h

number of kWh for 1 year = 0.006 × 3.0 × 365 = 6.57 kWh

Step 2: Calculate the cost.

cost = 6.57 × 8.1 = 53p (2 s.f.)

cost = £0.53 (2 s.f.)

Summary questions

1 State an alternative unit for W. *(1 mark)*
2 Calculate the current in a 2000 W, 240 V appliance. *(2 marks)*
3 Calculate the power dissipated by a 100 Ω resistor connected to a 240 V supply. *(2 marks)*
4 A 3000 W cooker is used for 4.0 hours. The cost of each kWh is 8.1p.
  Calculate the cost of using this cooker. *(2 marks)*

5 Calculate the heat energy in joules produced by a 60 W heater operated for 10 hours. *(2 marks)*
6 Calculate the resistance of the filament of a 12 V, 36 W lamp. *(2 marks)*

7 Use the definition of current and potential difference to show $P = VI$. *(3 marks)*
8 The power dissipated in a wire connected to a fixed power supply is 10 W.
  Calculate the power dissipated in the same wire connected to the same supply when it is pulled to double its original length. *(4 marks)*

Chapter 9 Practice questions

1 As the temperature of an NTC thermistor is increased, which statement is correct? Its resistance ...

   A increases because its volume increases

   B increases because it does not obey Ohm's law

   C decreases because there are more free electrons

   D decreases because the ions vibrate more. *(1 mark)*

2 The current in a $100\,\Omega$ resistor is $0.20\,A$.

   What is the energy dissipated by the resistor in a period of $3.0\,s$?

   A $4.0\,J$ C $20\,J$

   B $12\,J$ D $60\,J$ *(1 mark)*

3 A wire of length L and diameter d has resistance R.

   Another wire made from the same metal has length $4L$ and diameter $\frac{d}{2}$.

   What is the resistance of this new wire in terms of R?

   A R C $4R$

   B $2R$ D $16R$ *(1 mark)*

4 What are the base units for resistance?

   A $kg\,m\,s^{-2}$

   B $kg\,m^2\,s^{-1}$

   C $kg\,m^2\,A^{-1}\,s^{-1}$

   D $kg\,m^2\,A^{-2}\,s^{-3}$ *(1 mark)*

5 a Define resistance. *(1 mark)*

   b Figure 1 shows a graph of current I against potential difference V for a pencil 'lead' drawn by a student.

   The pencil lead is $9.0\,cm$ long and has diameter $0.82\,mm$.

   i Use Figure 1 to determine the resistance of the pencil lead. *(1 mark)*

   ii Calculate the resistivity of the material of the pencil lead. *(3 marks)*

   iii Calculate the current in the pencil lead when its ends are connected to a supply of e.m.f. $2.5\,V$ and negligible internal resistance. *(1 mark)*

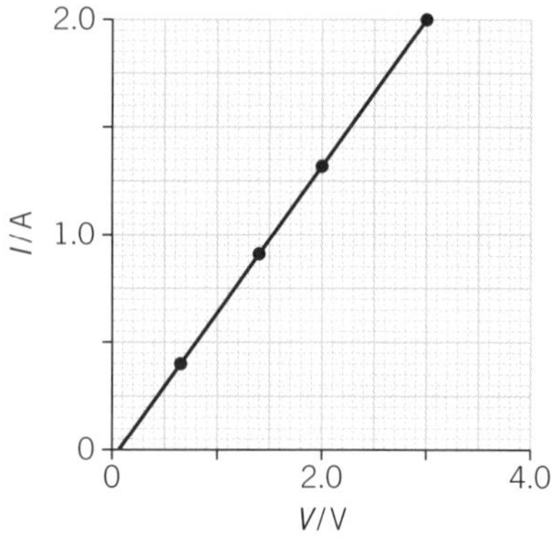

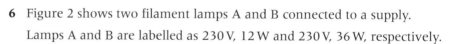

▲ Figure 1

6 Figure 2 shows two filament lamps A and B connected to a supply.

   Lamps A and B are labelled as $230\,V$, $12\,W$ and $230\,V$, $36\,W$, respectively.

   a Explain what is meant by $12\,W$. *(2 marks)*

   b Calculate the current in each lamp and therefore the total current delivered by the supply. *(3 marks)*

   c The lamps shown in Figure 2 are operated for 24 hours.

   Calculate the cost of operating the lamps given the cost of each kWh is 10.5p. *(3 marks)*

▲ Figure 2

7 Figure 3 shows a light-dependent resistor connected to a cell.

   The cell has negligible internal resistance.

   a Explain how the current I in the circuit changes as the intensity of the light falling on the LDR is decreased. *(2 marks)*

   b Explain whether the LDR will dissipate greater power when in darkness or in sunlight. *(2 marks)*

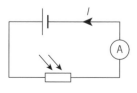

▲ Figure 3

Chapter 10 Electrical circuits

In this chapter you will learn about ...

- ☐ Kirchhoff's second law

- ☐ Series and parallel circuits

- ☐ Internal resistance

- ☐ Terminal p.d.

- ☐ Potential divider circuits

- ☐ Sensing circuits

10

ELECTRICAL CIRCUITS
10.1 Kirchhoff's laws and circuits
10.2 Combining resistors
10.3 Analysing circuits
Specification reference: 4.3.1

10.1 Kirchhoff's second law

You have already met Kirchhoff's first law in Topic 8.3. Kirchhoff's second law is a consequence of conservation of energy. Both laws are invaluable when analysing circuits.

The second law

Kirchhoff's second law: In any circuit, the sum of the electromotive forces is equal to the sum of the p.d.s around a closed loop.

This can be written mathematically as

$\Sigma \mathcal{E} = \Sigma V$ (Σ means 'sum of...')

or

$\Sigma \mathcal{E} = \Sigma IR$

where ε is the e.m.f., V is the p.d., and I is the current in a resistor of resistance R.

> **Revision tip**
>
> Kirchhoff's first law expresses conservation of *charge* and the second law expresses conservation of *energy*.

10.2 Combining resistors

Components can be connected in series (end-to-end), in parallel (across each other) or in a combination of series and parallel.

Series

▲ **Figure 1** *Resistors in series*

Figure 1 shows two resistors of resistance R_1 and R_2 connected in series.

Rules for a series circuit:

- The current I in each resistor is the same. (Kirchhoff's first law.)
- The total p.d. V across the resistors is the sum of the individual p.d.s. (Kirchhoff's second law.)

    $V = V_1 + V_2 + ...$

- The total resistance R of the combination is given by $R = R_1 + R_2 + ...$

Parallel

▲ **Figure 2** *Resistors in parallel*

Figure 2 shows two resistors of resistance R_1 and R_2 connected in parallel.

Rules for a parallel circuit:

- The current I is the sum of the individual currents. (Kirchhoff's first law.)

    $I = I_1 + I_2 + ...$

- The p.d. V across each resistor is the same. (Kirchhoff's second law.)
- The total resistance R of the combination is given by $\frac{1}{R} = \frac{1}{R_1} + \frac{1}{R_2} + ...$

> **Revision tip**
>
> For resistors in parallel, the total resistance is always less than the smallest resistance value.

> **Maths: The parallel rule**
>
> The parallel rule for resistors may be written as $R = (R_1^{-1} + R_2^{-1} + ...)^{-1}$. This is easier to do on a calculator.

10.3 Analysing circuits

There are some important equations and ideas you will need when analysing circuits.

Equations

- $I = \dfrac{\Delta Q}{\Delta t}$

- $W = VQ$

- $V = IR$

- $P = VI$ $\qquad$ $P = I^2R$ $\qquad$ $P = \dfrac{V^2}{R}$

- $R = R_1 + R_2 + \ldots$ $\qquad$ $\dfrac{1}{R} = \dfrac{1}{R_1} + \dfrac{1}{R_2} + \ldots$

Ideas

In a series circuit:

- the current in each component is the same
- the total p.d. across components is the sum of the p.d.s.

In a parallel circuit:

- the p.d. across each component is the same
- the total current is the sum of the currents.

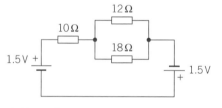
▲ Figure 3

 Worked example: Predicting p.d.

Calculate the p.d. across the 10 Ω resistor in Figure 3.

Step 1: Calculate the total resistance of the resistors in parallel.

$R = (R_1^{-1} + R_2^{-1})^{-1} = (12^{-1} + 18^{-1})^{-1} = 7.2\,\Omega$

Step 2: Calculate the total resistance of the circuit.

$R = R_1 + R_2 = 10 + 7.2 = 17.2\,\Omega$

Step 3: Use Kirchhoff's laws to calculate the current in the circuit.

The current I is the same and $\Sigma\varepsilon = \Sigma Ir$

$\therefore\ 1.5 + 1.5 = I \times 17.2$

$I = 0.174\,\text{A}$

Step 4: Use $V = IR$ to calculate the p.d. across the resistor.

$V = 0.174 \times 10$

$V = 1.7\,\text{V}\ (2\ \text{s.f.})$

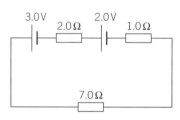
▲ Figure 4

Summary questions

1 You are given two 120 Ω resistors. Calculate the total resistance when these are connected in series and then in parallel. *(3 marks)*

2 A battery of e.m.f. 6.0 V is connected across 10 identical lamps. Calculate the p.d. across each lamp. *(1 mark)*

3 Calculate the total resistance and the e.m.f. for the circuit shown in Figure 4. *(2 marks)*

4 Calculate the current in the circuit shown in Figure 4 and the p.d. across the 7.0 Ω resistor. *(3 marks)*

5 A 100 Ω resistor is connected across a resistor of resistance R. A multimeter shows the total to be 70 Ω. Calculate the value of R. *(3 marks)*

6 A thermistor and a 100 Ω resistor are connected in series to a fixed power supply. The temperature of the thermistor is slowly decreased. Describe and explain the effect this has on the p.d. across the resistor. *(3 marks)*

10.4 Internal resistance
10.5 Potential divider circuits
10.6 Sensing circuits

Specification reference: 4.3.2, 4.3.3

10.4 Internal resistance

A source of e.m.f. has internal resistance. For example, a solar cell has internal resistance because the charges have to pass through the material of the cell.

Terminal p.d. and 'lost volts'

A source of e.m.f. can be represented by an e.m.f. ε in series with its internal resistance r. Figure 1 shows a source of e.m.f. providing current I to an external resistor, of resistance R.

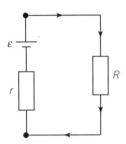

▲ **Figure 1** *A source of e.m.f. connected to an external 'load' of resistance R*

The current is the same in both resistors (Kirchhoff's first law). Using Kirchhoff's second law, we have

$$\varepsilon = IR + Ir \qquad \text{or} \qquad \varepsilon = I(R + r) \qquad \text{or} \qquad \varepsilon = V + Ir$$

where V is the terminal p.d., or simply the potential difference across the external resistor, and Ir is the p.d. across the internal resistor (which is also referred to as the 'lost volts').

Determining e.m.f. and internal resistance

You can get different I and V values by varying the value of R. Since $\varepsilon = V + Ir$, we have

$$V = -Ir + \varepsilon$$

The equation for a straight line is $y = mx + c$

Therefore, a graph of V against I will be a straight line with:

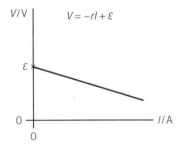

▲ **Figure 2** *The gradient of the graph is $-r$ and the V-intercept is ε*

- gradient = $-r$
- y-intercept = ε

10.5 Potential divider circuits

A potential divider circuit consists of two or more components connected to a battery or a power supply with the 'output' p.d. taken across one of the components, see Figure 3.

Potential divider equations

The output p.d. V_{out} is taken across the resistor of resistance R_2 – this is a fraction of the total p.d. V_{in} across the resistors. The bigger the resistance R_2 the larger is V_{out}.

The output p.d. is given by the equation

$$V_{out} = \frac{R_2}{R_1 + R_2} \times V_{in}$$

The current in the resistors is the same therefore

$$I = \frac{V_1}{R_1} = \frac{V_2}{R_2} \qquad \text{or} \qquad \frac{V_1}{V_2} = \frac{R_1}{R_2} \quad (V_1 \text{ and } V_2 \text{ are the p.d.s across the resistors})$$

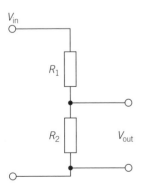

▲ **Figure 3** *A potential divider circuit*

10.6 Sensing circuits

You can use the potential divider equation to analyse a temperature-sensing circuit (Figure 4) and a light-sensing circuit (Figure 5).

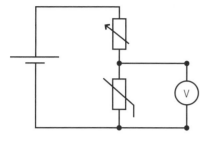

▲ **Figure 4** *Temperature-sensor has a thermistor*

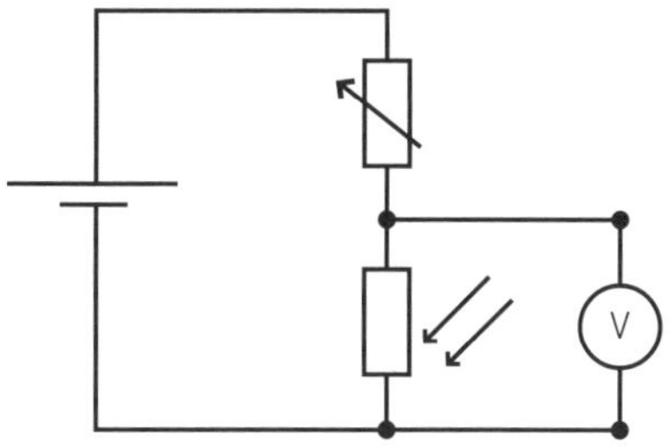

▲ **Figure 5** *Light-sensor has an LDR*

⊞ Worked example: Terminal p.d.

The battery in Figure 6 has e.m.f. 6.0 V and internal resistance 2.0 Ω. The maximum resistance of the variable resistor is 10 Ω. Calculate the maximum and minimum values of the terminal p.d.s.

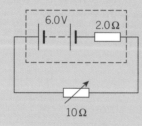

▲ **Figure 6**

Step 1: Calculate the maximum current and therefore the minimum terminal p.d.

$R = 0$; total resistance $= 0 + 2.0 = 2.0 \, \Omega$

$\text{current} = \dfrac{\varepsilon}{\text{total resistance}} = \dfrac{6.0}{2.0} = 3.0 \, \text{A}$

minimum terminal p.d. $V = IR = 3.0 \times 0 = 0 \, \text{V}$

Step 2: Calculate the minimum current and therefore the maximum terminal p.d.

$R = 10 \, \Omega$; total resistance $= 10 + 2.0 = 12.0 \, \Omega$

$\text{current} = \dfrac{\varepsilon}{\text{total resistance}} = \dfrac{6.0}{12.0} = 0.50 \, \text{A}$

maximum terminal p.d. $V = IR = 0.50 \times 10 = 5.0 \, \text{V}$ (2 s.f.)

Summary questions

1 Explain what is meant by 'lost volts'. *(1 mark)*

2 A cell of e.m.f. of 1.4 V is connected across a resistor. The terminal p.d. is 1.0 V.
  Explain why the p.d. across the resistor is not 1.4 V. *(2 marks)*

3 In **Q2** the resistor has resistance 20 Ω. Calculate the internal resistance r. *(2 marks)*

4 In the circuit shown in Figure 4, the cell has an e.m.f. of 1.5 V, the variable resistor is set to 100 Ω,
  and the resistance of the thermistor is 68 Ω. Calculate the voltmeter reading. *(2 marks)*

5 In Figure 3, $R_2 = 4R_1$. Calculate V_{out} in terms of V_{in}. *(2 marks)*

6 Explain how the calculation in **Q4** would be affected if the voltmeter has a finite resistance. *(3 marks)*

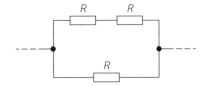

▲ Figure 1

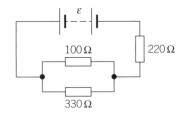

▲ Figure 2

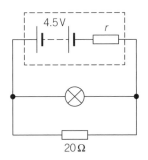

▲ Figure 3

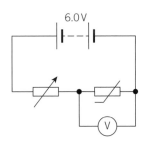

▲ Figure 4

1 A resistor is connected across a chemical cell.

Which statement is correct about terminal p.d.?

The terminal p.d. ...

   A is the 'lost volts'

   B is the e.m.f. of the cell

   C is the p.d across the external resistor

   D is the p.d. across the internal resistance. *(1 mark)*

2 Figure 1 shows part of a circuit with three resistors. The resistance of each resistor is R.

What is the total resistance of the circuit in terms of R?

   A $\dfrac{R}{3}$ **C** $\dfrac{2R}{3}$

   B $\dfrac{R}{2}$ **D** $3R$ *(1 mark)*

3 A battery of negligible internal resistance is connected to a resistor of resistance R. The current in the resistor is 3.0 A. A resistor of resistance $20\,\Omega$ is connected in series with the resistor of resistance R to the same battery. The current in the circuit is now 1.0 A.

What is the value of R?

   A $10\,\Omega$ **C** $30\,\Omega$

   B $20\,\Omega$ **D** $40\,\Omega$ *(1 mark)*

4 Figure 2 shows a circuit consisting of resistors.

The battery has negligible internal resistance.

The current in the $330\,\Omega$ resistor is 2.7 mA. Calculate:

   a the total resistance of the circuit; *(3 marks)*

   b the e.m.f. ε of the battery. *(4 marks)*

5 **a** State Kirchhoff's second law. *(1 mark)*

   b Figure 3 shows an electrical circuit.

     The battery has e.m.f. 4.5 V and internal resistance r. The potential difference across the filament lamp is 3.0 V and it dissipates energy at a rate of 0.60 W.

     Calculate:

     i the resistance of the lamp; *(2 marks)*

     ii the total resistance of the circuit connected across the terminals of the battery; *(2 marks)*

     iii the internal resistance r. *(2 marks)*

6 Figure 4 shows a potential divider circuit designed by a student to monitor the temperature of a room.

The battery has e.m.f. 6.0 V and negligible internal resistance. The digital voltmeter has an infinite resistance. The resistance of the variable resistor is adjusted to $120\,\Omega$. The current delivered by the battery is 15 mA when the thermistor is at room temperature.

   a Calculate the resistance of the thermistor at room temperature. *(3 marks)*

   b Describe the effect on the voltmeter reading when the resistance of the variable resistor is increased. The temperature of the thermistor is the same as before. *(3 marks)*

Chapter 11 Waves 1

In this chapter you will learn about ...

- ☐ Transverse and longitudinal waves

- ☐ Wave properties

- ☐ Reflection and diffraction

- ☐ Polarisation

- ☐ Intensity

- ☐ Electromagnetic waves

- ☐ Refraction and refractive index

- ☐ Critical angle

- ☐ Total internal reflection

11.1 Progressive waves

A progressive wave is an oscillation that travels through space. All progressive waves transfer energy from one place to another.

Two types of waves

In a **transverse wave** the oscillations or vibrations are perpendicular to the direction of energy transfer. (See Figure 1.)

In a **longitudinal wave** the oscillations are parallel to the direction of energy transfer. (See Figure 2.)

11.2 Wave properties

Several quantities are needed to describe and analyse waves. Learn the quantities defined in Table 1 and take care not to confuse them.

Definitions

▼ Table 1

Quantity and definition	Comments
Displacement is the distance from the equilibrium position in a particular direction.	Symbol → s; unit → m; a vector quantity
Amplitude is the maximum displacement of a wave. (See Figure 3.)	Symbol → A; unit → m
Wavelength is the distance between two adjacent points on a wave that are oscillating in phase (in step). (See Figure 3.)	Symbol → λ; unit → m; it is also the distance between adjacent peaks or troughs
Period is the time taken for the wave to move a distance of one whole wavelength.	Symbol → T; unit → s; it is also the time taken for a medium particle to make one complete oscillation
Frequency is the number of wavelengths passing though a point per unit time.	Symbol → f; unit → Hz; it is also the number of oscillations of a medium particle per unit time
Wave speed is the distance travelled by the wave per unit time.	Symbol → v; unit → m s^{-1}

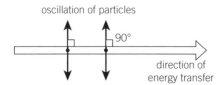

▲ **Figure 1** *Transverse*

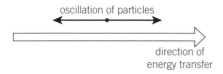

▲ **Figure 2** *Longitudinal*

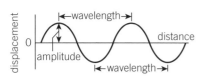

▲ **Figure 3** *A displacement–distance graph showing amplitude and wavelength*

Frequency and period

The relationship between period T and frequency f is $f = \dfrac{1}{T}$

For example, when $T = 0.010\,\text{s}$ then $f = \dfrac{1}{0.010} = 100\,\text{Hz}$.

Wave equation

The relationship between wave speed v, wavelength λ, and frequency f is called the wave equation. The wave equation $v = f\lambda$ can be used for any periodic wave.

Proof:

- Distance travelled by wave in one oscillation = λ.
- There are f oscillations per unit time.
- Therefore, distance travelled per unit time = wave speed $v = f \times \lambda$.

Graphs

A displacement–distance graph of the wave is a snapshot of the wave, see Figure 4.

Imagine the wave travelling to the right. After a time of one period T, the peak A will be where peak E is shown.

A displacement–time graph of the wave shows the motion of a specific point in the medium, see Figure 5. The time for one complete oscillation is the period T.

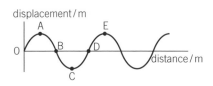

▲ **Figure 4** *A displacement–distance graph of a wave*

Phase difference

Phase difference is the fraction of an oscillation between two oscillating particles.

The term phase difference can be used for two points on two different waves or along the same wave.

Phase difference is measured in degrees or in radians, see Table 2.

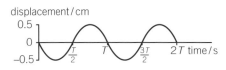

▲ **Figure 5** *A displacement–time graph shows the oscillations of a specific particle*

 ▼ **Table 2**

separation between points	phase difference / °	phase difference / rad
λ	360	π
$\dfrac{\lambda}{2}$	180	$\dfrac{\pi}{2}$
$\dfrac{\lambda}{4}$	90	$\dfrac{\pi}{4}$
x	$\dfrac{x}{\lambda} \times 360$	$\dfrac{x}{\lambda} \times 2\pi$

> **Maths: Angles**
>
> $2\pi = 360°$ therefore 1 rad = 57.3°

🖩 Worked example: What can we hear?

The audible frequency range for humans is 20 Hz to 20 kHz.

Calculate the longest and shortest wavelengths humans can hear.

speed of sound in air = 340 m s^{-1}

Step 1: Use the wave equation to calculate the longest wavelength.

$$v = 340 \text{ m s}^{-1} \qquad f = 20 \text{ Hz} \qquad \lambda = ?$$

$$\lambda = \frac{v}{f} = \frac{340}{20} = 17\text{ m}$$

Step 2: Use the wave equation to calculate the shortest wavelength.

$$v = 340 \text{ m s}^{-1} \qquad f = 20 \times 10^3 \text{ Hz} \qquad \lambda = ?$$

$$\lambda = \frac{v}{f} = \frac{340}{20 \times 10^3} = 1.7 \times 10^{-2}\text{ m}$$

The longest wavelength is 17 m and the shortest wavelength is 1.7 cm (2 s.f.).

Summary questions

1 Explain what is meant by a frequency of 10 Hz. *(1 mark)*
2 A wave has wavelength of 2.0 cm. State the distance travelled by the wave in one period. *(1 mark)*

3 Water waves have frequency 30 Hz and wavelength 4.0 cm. Calculate the speed of the water waves. *(1 mark)*
4 Bats can emit sound waves of frequency 150 kHz. The speed of sound is 340 m s^{-1}.
   Calculate the wavelength corresponding to this frequency. *(2 marks)*

5 Use Figure 4 to determine the phase difference between points:
   a B and D; *(2 marks)*
   b A and D. *(2 marks)*
6 A wave has a wavelength of 20 cm. Calculate the distance between two points with a phase difference of 300°. *(2 marks)*

11.3 Reflection and refraction
11.4 Diffraction and polarisation

Specification reference: 4.4.1

11.3 Reflection and refraction

All progressive waves can be reflected and refracted.

Reflection

Reflection occurs when a wave changes direction at a boundary between two different media, remaining in the original medium.

Light is reflected when you look at yourself in the mirror. Figure 1 shows the reflection of a wave. The separation between adjacent wavefronts is equal to the wavelength. A wavefront is a line joining all neighbouring points oscillating in phase.

- The incident and reflected rays are in the same plane.
- The angle of incidence is equal to the angle of reflection. (The angles are measured relative to the normal – dotted line.)

Refraction

Refraction occurs when a wave changes direction as it changes speed when it passes from one medium to another.

Refraction will be covered more in Topic 8.3, Refractive index.

Figure 2 shows the refraction of water waves at the boundary between deep and shallow water.

- The frequency of the refracted waves remains constant.
- The speed, and therefore the wavelength, of the wave changes.

11.4 Diffraction and polarisation

All waves can be diffracted. Only transverse waves can be polarised.

Diffraction

Diffraction is the spreading of a wave when it passing through a narrow gap or around an obstacle.

Figure 3 shows the diffraction of a wave at a gap.

- The speed, wavelength, and frequency of a wave do not change when diffraction occurs.
- There is significant diffraction when the width of the gap is similar to the wavelength of the incident wave. There is very little diffraction when the wavelength is much much smaller than the width of the gap.

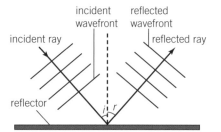

▲ **Figure 1** *Reflection*

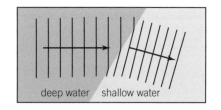

▲ **Figure 2** *Refraction*

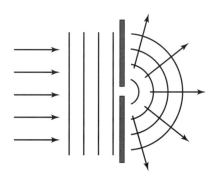

▲ **Figure 3** *Diffraction*

Polarisation

A plane polarised wave has oscillations in one plane only.

Ordinary light is unpolarised with oscillations in many planes at right angles to the direction of travel. Unpolarised light passing through a single polarising filter (Polaroid) will be plane polarised. Figure 4 shows polarised and unpolarised oscillations.

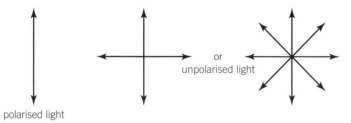

or
unpolarised light

polarised light

▲ **Figure 4** *Polarised and unpolarised*

You can show polarisation effects using two polarising filters. Figure 5 shows the effects of using two polarising filters. In (a), the transmission axes of the filters are aligned – light passing through the filters is plane polarised. In (c), the transmission axes of the filters are at right angles – light is blocked by the overlapping filter.

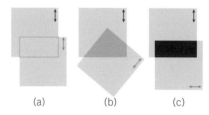

(a)   (b)   (c)

▲ **Figure 5** *Using polarising filters*

🖩 Worked example: What can we hear?

Estimate the frequency of sound that can be diffracted at a slit of width 3.0 cm. The speed of sound in air is 340 m s⁻¹.

Step 1: Estimate the wavelength of sound.

The wavelength λ must be similar to the width for diffraction to occur. Therefore, λ is about 3.0 cm.

Step 2: Write down the quantities given.

$v = 340 \, \text{m s}^{-1}$ $\lambda \approx 3.0 \times 10^{-2} \, \text{m}$ $f = ?$

Step 3: Use the wave equation to estimate the frequency f of sound.

$$f = \frac{v}{\lambda} = \frac{340}{3.0 \times 10^{-2}} = 1.13 \times 10^4 \, \text{Hz}$$

The frequency is about 11 kHz (2 s.f.).

Summary questions

1   State the quantities that remain the same when light is reflected
    off a mirror.   (*1 mark*)
2   Explain why sound cannot be polarised.   (*1 mark*)

3   A slit has a gap of width 1.0 cm. State which of the following
    waves can be diffracted.
    a   Light of wavelength 500 nm   (*1 mark*)
    b   Microwaves of wavelength 3.0 cm.   (*1 mark*)
4   State one quantity that changes when a wave refracts.   (*1 mark*)

5   Draw a diagram to show the diffraction of parallel wavefronts
    at the edge of an obstacle.   (*1 mark*)
6   Use Figure 6 to state and explain the change of wavelength
    as light travels from glass into water.   (*3 marks*)

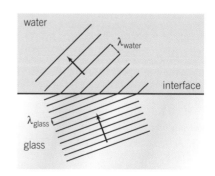

water

λ_{water}

interface

λ_{glass}

glass

▲ **Figure 6**

11.5 Intensity

Sunlight incident at the top of the Earth's atmosphere delivers about 1 kW of power per m² or 1kW m⁻². This is the intensity of sunlight. Intensity must not be confused with power or energy.

Intensity

The **intensity** of a progressive wave is defined as the radiant power passing at right angles through a surface per unit area.

Intensity is measured in watts per square metre ($\mathrm{W\,m^{-2}}$). The equation relating intensity I, area A, and incident radiant power P is

$$I = \frac{P}{A}$$

Inverse square law

The intensity from a point source of power P decreases with distance r from the source as the power spreads over a larger surface area. The intensity is given by

$$I = \frac{P}{4\pi r^2} \propto \frac{1}{r^2}$$

The intensity obeys an inverse square with distance.

You can use the expression above for the Sun, a filament lamp, and so on.

Intensity and amplitude

The intensity I for a wave is related to the amplitude A of the wave by the following expression

$I \propto A^2$

This means that doubling the amplitude of the wave will quadruple the intensity.

11.6 Electromagnetic waves

Light is just a small part of the spectrum of electromagnetic (EM) waves. Figure 1 shows the electromagnetic spectrum with typical wavelengths of the various regions or principal radiations.

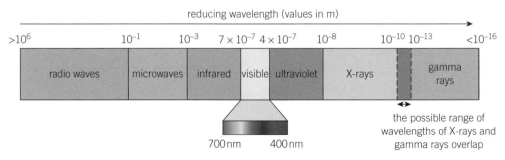

▲ **Figure 1** *The electromagnetic spectrum showing the principal radiations or regions*

Electromagnetic spectrum and properties of EM waves

All electromagnetic waves:

- can travel though a vacuum
- travel at the speed c of $3.0 \times 10^8\,\text{m s}^{-1}$ in a vacuum
- are transverse waves
- consist of oscillating magnetic and electric fields at right angles to each other.

You can use the wave equation $c = f\lambda$, where f is the frequency of the electromagnetic wave of wavelength λ.

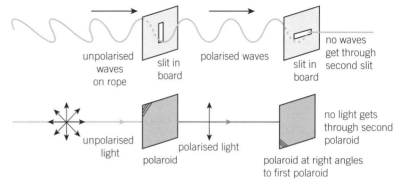

▲ **Figure 2** *Polarisation of light*

11.7 Polarisation of electromagnetic waves

You have already met the idea of plane polarised waves in Topic 11.4, Diffraction and polarisation. All electromagnetic waves can be plane polarised because they are all transverse waves.

Light

Visible light can be plane polarised using polarising filters (Polaroid). Figure 2 compares the polarisation of unpolarised waves on a rope and unpolarised light.

Microwaves

The microwave transmitters available in schools and colleges produce plane polarised waves with the electric field oscillating in the vertical plane. In order to show the transmission and absorption of these polarised waves you have to use a metal grille, see Figure 3.

▲ **Figure 3** *A metal grille can be used to show polarisation effects*

- With the metal grille horizontal (as in Figure 3), the vertically plane polarised microwaves are transmitted through the grille.
- With the metal grille vertical, the vertically plane polarised microwaves are absorbed by the free electrons within the metal rods of the grille and therefore there is almost no transmission.

🖩 Worked example: Aerial

The length of an aerial used for detecting radio waves is about half the wavelength of the radio waves.

Calculate the length of an aerial for detecting radio waves of frequency 60 MHz.

Step 1: Use the wave equation to calculate the wavelength of the radio waves.

$$c = 3.0 \times 10^8\,\text{m s}^{-1} \qquad f = 60 \times 10^6\,\text{Hz} \qquad \lambda = ?$$

$$\lambda = \frac{c}{f} = \frac{3.0 \times 10^8}{60 \times 10^6} = 5.0\,\text{m}$$

Step 2: Calculate the length of the aerial.

$$\text{length} = \frac{\lambda}{2} = \frac{5.0}{2}$$

$$\text{length} = 2.5\,\text{m (2 s.f.)}$$

Summary questions

1 State the unit of power and intensity. *(1 mark)*
2 Explain why electromagnetic waves can be plane polarised. *(1 mark)*
3 State and explain the effect on the intensity of a wave when its amplitude is halved. *(2 marks)*
4 Identify an electromagnetic wave that has frequency of 1.5×10^{17} Hz. *(3 marks)*
5 The radiant power incident on the surface of the Earth from the Sun is about $1050\,\text{W m}^{-2}$. The Earth is at a distance of 1.5×10^{11} m from the Sun. Estimate the total power emitted by the Sun. *(3 marks)*
6 A solar panel of $1.2\,\text{m}^2$ has an efficiency of 20%. Use the information given in Q5 to estimate the number of solar panels required to produce an electrical output of 1.0 kW. *(3 marks)*

11.8 Refractive index

A ray of light incident at an angle to the boundary between two transparent materials will be reflected and refracted at this boundary. Refraction occurs because the speed of light changes as it enters a different material. The angle of refraction depends on the refractive index of each material.

Definition

The **refractive index** of a transparent material is defined as the speed of light in a vacuum divided by the speed of light in the material.

The refractive index n of a material is given by the equation

$$n = \frac{c}{v}$$

where c is the speed of light in a vacuum and v is the speed in the material. Refractive index has no unit. By definition, $n = 1$ for vacuum. For air $n = 1.0003 \approx 1.00$ (3 s.f.) and for glass about 1.5 (2 s.f.).

> **Revision tip**
> The refractive index of a material can never be less than 1.

Refraction law

Figure 1 shows the path of a ray of light travelling from a material of refractive index n_1 into another material of refractive index n_2. The ray of light is refracted at the boundary. The incidence angle θ_1 and refracted angle θ_2 are measured relative to the normal.

Experiments show that

$$n_1 \sin \theta_1 = n_2 \sin \theta_2$$

Figure 2 shows an arrangement used to investigate refraction in the laboratory.

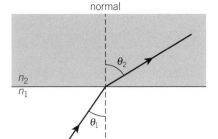

▲ **Figure 1** *Refraction at a boundary (the reflected ray is not shown)*

With $n_1 \approx 1.00$, $\theta_1 = i$ (angle of incidence), $\theta_2 = r$ (angle of refraction), and $n_2 = n$ (refractive index of glass), we can use the equation below to determine the refractive index of the glass.

$$1.00 \times \sin i = n \sin r$$

or

$$n = \frac{\sin i}{\sin r}$$

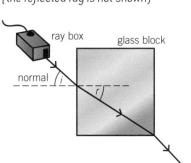

▲ **Figure 2** *An arrangement used to determine the refractive index of glass*

11.9 Total internal reflection

There is no refraction when **total internal reflection** (TIR) of light occurs at the boundary between two transparent materials. All the energy of the wave is returned back into the material. See Figure 3.

Total internal reflection only takes place when:

● light in a material travels towards a material of lower refractive index
● the angle of incidence is greater than the critical angle.

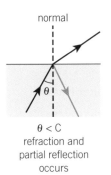 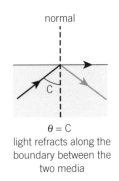 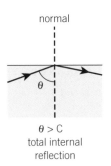

$\theta < C$
refraction and
partial reflection
occurs

$\theta = C$
light refracts along the
boundary between the
two media

$\theta > C$
total internal
reflection

▲ **Figure 3** *Refraction and total internal reflection*

Critical angle

Consider light incident at the boundary between a material and air. The refractive index of the material is n. At the critical angle C the angle of refraction is 90°.

The refraction law $n_1 \sin \theta_1 = n_2 \sin \theta_2$ gives

$n \times \sin C = 1.00 \times \sin 90°$ (n_2 for air is 1.00)

or

$\sin C = \dfrac{1}{n}$

 Worked example: Diamonds in water

Diamonds are submerged into water. The refractive index of diamond is 2.42 and the refractive index of water is 1.33. Calculate the critical angle for light in diamond.

Step 1: Write down the quantities given in the question.

$n_1 = 2.42$ $\theta_2 = C$ $n_2 = 1.33$ $\theta_2 = 90°$

Step 2: Use the refraction law to calculate the critical angle.

$n_1 \sin \theta_1 = n_2 \sin \theta_2$

$2.42 \times \sin C = 1.33 \times \sin 90°$ ($\sin 90° = 1$)

$\sin C = 0.550$

$C = 33°$ (2 s.f.)

Summary questions

1 State the refractive index of a vacuum. *(1 mark)*
2 The speed of light in a transparent material is $0.50\,c$, where c is the speed of light in a vacuum.
   Calculate the refractive index of the material. *(1 mark)*

3 According to a student there will be total internal reflection of light travelling from air into glass.
   Explain why this is incorrect. *(2 marks)*
4 The refractive index of glass is 1.50. Calculate the speed of light in a glass block. *(2 marks)*

5 Light travels from air into a transparent material. The angle of incidence is 70° and the angle of refraction is 35°. Calculate the refractive index of the material. *(2 marks)*
6 Use the information given in the worked example to calculate the critical angle for light in diamond when the diamond is in air. *(3 marks)*

1 Which is the correct order for the increasing frequencies of the following electromagnetic waves?

   A infrared   ultraviolet   X-rays   microwaves

   B X-rays   infrared   ultraviolet   microwaves

   C ultraviolet   microwaves   infrared   X-rays

   D microwaves   infrared   ultraviolet   X-rays   *(1 mark)*

2 Which statement is correct about light from a laser travelling from air into glass?

   A The speed of light increases.

   B The intensity of light increases.

   C The frequency remains the same.

   D The wavelength of light decreases.   *(1 mark)*

3 What is the frequency of an electromagnetic wave of wavelength 30 μm?

   A 1.0×10^{10} Hz

   B 1.0×10^{13} Hz

   C 1.0×10^{16} Hz

   D 1.0×10^{19} Hz   *(1 mark)*

4 Light travels from a transparent material of refractive index 1.75 towards the boundary between the material and the air. The refractive index of air is 1.00.

   What is the critical angle for light in the material?

   A 30°

   B 35°

   C 55°

   D 60°   *(1 mark)*

5 **a** State two properties of electromagnetic waves.   *(2 marks)*

   b A space probe close to Jupiter emits a radio signal of frequency 8.0 GHz.

     Jupiter is about 6.3×10^{11} m away from the Earth.

     i Calculate the wavelength of the electromagnetic wave emitted by the probe.   *(2 marks)*

     ii Identify the part of the electromagnetic spectrum the waves in i belong to.   *(1 mark)*

     iii Estimate the time taken for the signal to travel from the probe to the Earth.   *(2 marks)*

6 **a** Explain what is meant by the statement

     The refractive index of glass is 1.54.   *(1 mark)*

   b Calculate the speed of light in the glass in (a).   *(1 mark)*

   c Figure 1 shows light from a laser incident at the boundary between water and the glass from (a).

     The refractive index of water is 1.33. The angle of incidence of the light in the water is 40°.

     i Calculate the angle of refraction.   *(3 marks)*

     ii Complete Figure 1 to show the refraction and reflection of light at the boundary.   *(2 marks)*

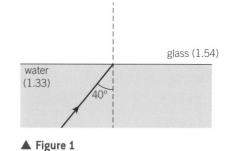

glass (1.54)

water (1.33)

40°

▲ **Figure 1**

Chapter 12 Waves 2

In this chapter you will learn about ...

- [ ] Superposition of waves
- [ ] Coherence
- [ ] Constructive and destructive Interference
- [ ] Path difference
- [ ] Phase difference
- [ ] The Young double-slit experiment
- [ ] Stationary waves
- [ ] Harmonics

WAVES 2
12.1 Superposition of waves
12.2 Interference
12.3 The Young double-slit experiment

Specification reference: 4.4.3

12.1 Superposition of waves

When two or more progressive waves meet, they combine and then pass through each other. The term used for waves of the same type combining is called superposition.

Principle of superposition of waves

The **principle of superposition** states that when two waves meet at a point the resultant displacement at that point is equal to the sum of the displacements of the individual waves.

For example, if the displacements at a point from two waves are $-2.1\,\text{cm}$ and $+5.0\,\text{cm}$, then the resultant displacement is simply $+2.9\,\text{cm}$.

12.2 Interference

Coherence refers to waves emitted from two sources having a constant phase difference.

All coherent sources emit waves of the same type, same frequency, and wavelength.

Path difference and phase difference

Interference is the superposition of waves from two coherent sources.

Figure 1 shows laser light incident at two narrow slits S_1 and S_2. The light is diffracted at each slit and interference occurs where the diffracted waves overlap. The slits behave as coherent sources. The type of interference, constructive or destructive, at point P depends on the path difference or the phase difference, see Table 1. The path difference is the extra distance travelled by one of the waves from the slits, that is,

$$\text{path difference} = S_1P - S_2P$$

▲ **Figure 1** *Interference of waves diffracted at narrow slits*

▼ Table 1

Type of interference	Observation at P	Path difference in terms of wavelength λ	Phase difference
Constructive $\curvearrowright + \curvearrowright = \curvearrowright$	Light: bright 'fringe' Sound: loud sound Microwaves: large signal	$0, \lambda, 2\lambda, \dots n\lambda$ (n is an integer)	$0°$ or 2π rad
Destructive $\curvearrowright + \curvearrowleft = \underline{\qquad}$	Light: dark 'fringe' Sound: quiet sound Microwaves: small signal	$\frac{\lambda}{2}, \frac{3\lambda}{2}, \dots (n + \frac{\lambda}{2})\lambda$ (n is an integer)	$180°$ or π rad

Common misconception

Path difference and phase difference are often confused. Path difference is a *length* and phase difference is an *angular measurement* in degrees or radians.

12.3 The Young double-slit experiment

The Young double-slit experiment uses two narrow slits to determine the wavelength of monochromatic light.

Light

Figures 2 and 3 show two arrangements for the Young double-slit experiment. The wavelength λ of the monochromatic light can be determined using the equation

$$\lambda = \frac{ax}{D} \qquad (a \ll D)$$

where a is the separation between the narrow slits, x is the separation between adjacent bright (or dark) fringes, and D is the separation between the slits and the screen.

Microwaves and sound

The equation $\lambda = \frac{ax}{D}$ and the arrangement shown in Figure 4 can be used to determine the wavelength of microwaves. For determining the wavelength of sound, the slits are replaced by two loudspeakers connected to the same signal generator and the sound is detected using a microphone connected either to an intensity-meter or an oscilloscope.

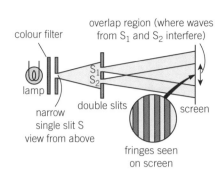

▲ **Figure 2** *Young double-slit experiment using a filament lamp and colour filter*

▲ **Figure 3** *Young double-slit experiment using a laser*

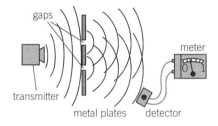

▲ **Figure 4** *Experiment to determine wavelength of microwaves*

> **Worked example: Fringes**
>
> Describe the effect on the fringes observed in a Young double-slit experiment when the separation between the slits is decreased.
>
> **Step 1:** Write the equation for the fringe separation x.
>
> $$x = \frac{\lambda D}{a}$$
>
> **Step 2:** Carefully describe the effect on the fringes using the equation above.
>
> The fringe separation x is inversely proportional to the separation a between the slits.
>
> Therefore, the fringe pattern spreads out when the separation between the slits is decreased.

Summary questions

1 Explain what is meant by coherent sources. *(1 mark)*
2 Describe constructive interference in terms of path difference and phase difference. *(2 marks)*

3 The waves shown in Figure 1 have wavelength λ of 2.0 cm. State and explain the type of interference at point P when:
 a $S_1P = 11.0$ cm and $S_2P = 7.0$ cm; *(2 marks)*
 b $S_1P = 7.2$ cm and $S_2P = 6.2$ cm *(2 marks)*
4 Use the results below from a Young double-slit experiment to calculate the wavelength.
 $a = 0.10$ mm $\qquad x = 3.1$ cm $\qquad D = 6.20$ m *(2 marks)*

5 Red light of wavelength 650 nm incident at two slits produces bright fringes separated by 5.2 mm. The same arrangement produces bright fringes separated by 4.1 mm when green light is used. Calculate the wavelength of this green light. *(2 marks)*
6 In Q4, estimate the absolute uncertainty in the wavelength. *(3 marks)*

12.4 Stationary waves
12.5 Harmonics
12.6 Stationary waves in air columns

Specification reference: 4.4.4

12.4 Stationary waves

A stationary (or standing) wave is the result of superposition of two progressive waves with the same frequency (and ideally the same amplitude) travelling in opposite directions. All waves can produce stationary waves.

Understanding stationary waves

Figure 1 shows a stationary wave on a stretched string with three 'loops'. The profile of the string is the result of superposition of progressive waves travelling to the left and to the right. The progressive and stationary waves have the same period T and frequency f.

At time $t = 0$, the two progressive waves combine constructively, at time $t = \frac{T}{4}$, they combine destructively, and so on.

Some important points:

- A stationary wave has nodes and antinodes. A **node** is a point that has zero amplitude and an **antinode** is a point of maximum amplitude.
- separation between adjacent nodes (or antinodes) = $\frac{\lambda}{2}$
- separation between adjacent node and antinode = $\frac{\lambda}{4}$
- You can determine the speed v of the **progressive wave** using the wave equation $v = f\lambda$.

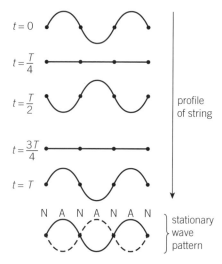

▲ **Figure 1** *A typical stationary wave pattern on a string*

Comparing progressive and stationary waves

Table 1 compares progressive and stationary waves.

▼ **Table 1**

	Progressive wave	Stationary wave
Energy transfer	Yes	No
Frequency	The same for all points.	The same for all points, except at the nodes where it is zero.
Amplitude	The same for all points.	Varies from zero at the nodes to maximum at the antinodes.
Phase difference ϕ between two points	$\phi = \frac{x}{\lambda}\,360°$ where x is the separation between the points.	$\phi = 180°n$ where n is the number of nodes between the points.

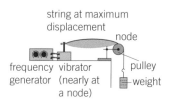

▲ **Figure 2** *Stationary waves on a stretched string*

12.5 Harmonics

Figure 2 shows how stationary waves can be produced on a stretched string. The transverse waves on the string are reflected at the pulley-end. These reflected waves combine with those from the vibrator to produce the stationary waves.

Understanding harmonics

Figure 3 shows the first three stationary wave patterns produced on the stretched string – these are called harmonics.

N = node   A = antinode
(dotted line shows string half a cycle earlier)

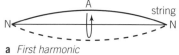

a *First harmonic*

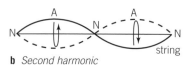

b *Second harmonic*

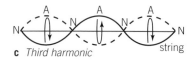

c *Third harmonic*

▲ **Figure 3** *Stationary wave patterns*

The **fundamental frequency** of the stationary wave is the lowest frequency of vibration for a given arrangement.

The first harmonic (fundamental mode of vibration) is a stationary wave that has frequency equal to the fundamental frequency. All other harmonics have a frequency that is a multiple of the fundamental frequency.

Figure 4 shows how stationary waves can be investigated using microwaves.

12.6 Stationary waves in air columns

Sound resonates at certain frequencies in an air-filled tube. You can produce a loud sound by holding a vibrating tuning fork close to the open end of a tube and adjusting the length of the air column.

Closed and open tubes

Figures 5 and 6 show the stationary waves produced in a tube open at only one end and in a tube open at both ends.

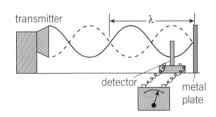

▲ **Figure 4** *Microwaves can also produce stationary waves*

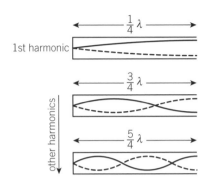

▲ **Figure 5** *Stationary waves in a tube open at only one end*

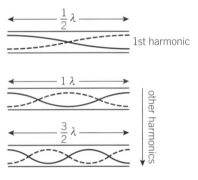

▲ **Figure 6** *Stationary waves in a tube open at both ends*

 Worked example: Vibrating string

A string is stretched between two points separated by 15 cm. The string vibrates at a fundamental frequency of 120 Hz. Calculate the speed of the progressive waves on the string.

Step 1: Determine the wavelength of the progressive wave.

separation between successive nodes = 15 cm

Therefore, $\lambda = 2 \times 15 = 30$ cm

Step 2: Use the wave equation to determine the speed v of sound.

$v = ?$ $f = 120$ Hz $\lambda = 0.30$ m

$v = f\lambda = 120 \times 0.30$

$v = 36$ m s^{-1} (2 s.f.)

Summary questions

1 State the phase difference of all points between adjacent nodes of a stationary wave.   *(1 mark)*

2 The separation between adjacent node and antinode is 10 cm. State and explain the wavelength of the progressive wave.   *(2 marks)*

3 Explain how a stationary wave is produced in the arrangement shown in Figure 4.   *(2 marks)*

4 The separation between adjacent antinodes of a string is 28 cm. The string vibrates at 60 Hz.
Calculate the speed of the progressive waves on the string.   *(3 marks)*

5 The length of the tube in Figure 5 is 30 cm. The speed of sound is 340 m s^{-1}. Calculate the fundamental frequency.   *(3 marks)*

6 In Figure 6, the third harmonic has frequency 500 Hz. Calculate the length of the tube.   *(3 marks)*

Chapter 12 Practice questions

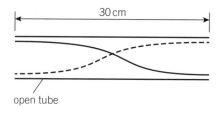

open tube

▲ Figure 1

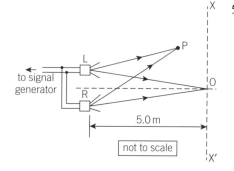

▲ Figure 2

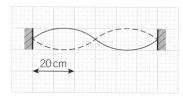

▲ Figure 3

1 Figure 1 shows a stationary wave drawn by a student for sound waves in an open tube.

What is the wavelength of the sound wave?

   A 15 cm   **B** 30 cm   **C** 45 cm   **D** 60 cm   *(1 mark)*

2 Two progressive waves, of the same wavelength of 2.0 cm, combine together. The path difference between the two waves is 0.5 cm.

What is the phase difference between these two waves?

   A 45°   **B** 90°   **C** 180°   **D** 270°   *(1 mark)*

3 In the Young double-slit experiment with monochromatic light, the distance between the screen and the slits is decreased.

Which statement is correct about adjacent bright fringes seen on the screen?

   A There is no change.

   B Their colour changes.

   C They get further apart.

   D They get closer together.   *(1 mark)*

4 A microwave transmitter is placed in front of a metal sheet. A stationary wave is formed between the metal sheet and the transmitter with adjacent nodes separated by 3.0 cm.

What is the frequency of the microwaves?

   A 5.0×10^7 Hz   **C** 5.0×10^9 Hz

   B 1.0×10^8 Hz   **D** 1.0×10^{10} Hz   *(1 mark)*

5 a Explain what is meant by a progressive wave.   *(1 mark)*

   b Figure 2 shows two loudspeakers L and R connected to the same signal generator.

     i Explain the common feature of the sound waves emitted from L and R.   *(1 mark)*

     ii At point P, a microphone picks up a strong signal. Explain this in terms of interference of the waves from L and R.   *(2 marks)*

     iii The separation between the loudspeakers is 1.4 m. The frequency of sound emitted from the loudspeakers is 4.0 kHz. The microphone is now moved along the straight line from X to X'. This line is 5.0 m from the loudspeakers. The separation between adjacent regions of loud sound along XX' is 30 cm.

     Calculate:

     1 the wavelength of sound;   *(3 marks)*

     2 the speed of sound.   *(2 marks)*

6 A student connects one end of a string to an oscillator and fixes the other end to a stand. The frequency of the oscillator is adjusted to 110 Hz. Figure 3 shows the sketch of the stationary wave observed by the student.

   a Use Figure 3 to determine the speed of the progressive waves on the string.   *(3 marks)*

   b The frequency of the oscillator is increased slightly.

   Suggest what happens to the profile of the string.   *(1 mark)*

   c The frequency of the oscillator is increased further until a stationary wave with three 'loops' is produced. Predict the frequency of the oscillator.   *(3 marks)*

Chapter 13 Quantum physics

In this chapter you will learn about ...

- [ ] Photons
- [ ] Electronvolt
- [ ] Photoelectric effect
- [ ] Work function
- [ ] Threshold frequency
- [ ] Einstein's photoelectric equation
- [ ] Wave–particle duality
- [ ] De Broglie waves
- [ ] Electron diffraction

13

QUANTUM PHYSICS
13.1 The photon model
13.2 The photoelectric effect
Specification reference: 4.5.1, 4.5.2

13.1 The photon model

Electromagnetic waves travel through space as waves – the diffraction and interference of electromagnetic waves provides evidence for this. However, when electromagnetic waves interact with matter, they do so as packets of discrete energy called photons.

A **photon** is a quantum of electromagnetic energy.

Photons

The quantum of energy E of a photon is related to the frequency f and wavelength λ of electromagnetic radiation by the following equations

$$E = hf \quad \text{and} \quad E = \frac{hc}{\lambda}$$

where h is the Planck constant and c is the speed of light in a vacuum. The experimental value for h is 6.63×10^{-34} J s.

Electronvolts

The **electronvolt** (eV) is a convenient unit of energy when dealing with particles and photons.

The electronvolt is defined as the energy gained by an electron travelling through a potential difference of 1 volt.

1 eV = potential difference × charge on electron = 1.0 V × 1.60×10^{-19} C

1 eV = 1.60×10^{-19} J

> **Revision tip**
> Multiply by 1.60×10^{-19} when converting from eV to J, and divide by 1.60×10^{-19} when converting from J to eV.

LEDs and h

An LED emits light when the potential difference across it exceeds a threshold p.d. (voltage) V. Photons are emitted when electrons within the LED lose energy. A single photon is produced when a single electron transfers energy.

energy transferred by electron ≈ energy of photon

$$eV \approx \frac{hc}{\lambda}$$

Different colour emitting diodes can be used to determine an approximate value for the Planck constant.

- Plot a graph of threshold p.d. V against $\frac{1}{\lambda}$
- The gradient G of the straight line through the origin should be equal to $\frac{hc}{e}$
- Therefore, $h \approx \frac{Ge}{c}$

13.2 The photoelectric effect

Electromagnetic radiation can be used to remove electrons from the surface of metals. This effect is known as the **photoelectric effect**. A negatively charged gold-leaf electroscope and zinc plate can be used to demonstrate this effect, see Figure 1.

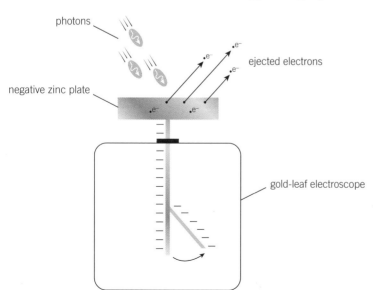

photons

ejected electrons

negative zinc plate

gold-leaf electroscope

▲ **Figure 1** *A gold-leaf electroscope*

Observations:

- Visible light, no matter how intense, does not remove electrons from the zinc plate.
- Ultraviolet radiation, even of very low intensity, instantaneously ejects electrons from the zinc plate. The gold-leaf collapses as photoelectrons are removed.

Work function and threshold frequency

The wave model cannot explain the observations above because intensity, and not frequency, should be the factor that should govern the removal of electrons. You need to know about work function and threshold frequency to understand the photoelectric effect.

The **work function** of a metal is the minimum energy required to free an electron from the surface of the metal.

The **threshold frequency** is the minimum frequency of the incident electromagnetic radiation that will free electrons from the surface of the metal.

Quantum rules

- A single photon can only interact with a single electron on the surface of the metal.
- Energy is conserved in the photon–electron interaction.
- An electron is only released when the photon energy hf is equal, or greater than, the work function ϕ of the metal.
- At the threshold frequency f_0, energy of photon = work function.
- Intensity of the incident radiation is related to the number of photons per unit time – doubling the intensity doubles the number of photons per unit time.

Worked example: Threshold frequency

The work function of a metal is 4.90 eV. Calculate the threshold frequency for this metal.

Step 1: Calculate the work function in joules (J).

$\phi = 4.90 \times 1.60 \times 10^{-19} = 7.84 \times 10^{-19}$ J

Step 2: Calculate the threshold frequency f_0.

energy of photon = work function

$hf_0 = \phi$

$f_0 = \dfrac{7.84 \times 10^{-19}}{6.63 \times 10^{-34}} = 1.18 \times 10^{15}$ Hz (3 s.f.)

Summary questions

1 State the SI unit of work function. (1 mark)
2 Convert 100 eV into J. (1 mark)
3 State the energy in eV gained by an electron travelling through a p.d. of 1000 V. (1 mark)

4 Suggest why visible light incident on a zinc plate cannot eject any electrons. (1 mark)
5 Calculate the wavelength of a photon of energy 8.0×10^{-19} J. (3 marks)

6 An LED emits light of wavelength 560 nm. The radiant power of the LED is 40 mW. Calculate the number of photons emitted from the LED per second. (4 marks)
7 The work function of a metal is 4.30 eV. Electromagnetic radiation of wavelength 400 nm is incident on the metal. Explain if this radiation produces any photoelectrons. (4 marks)

13.3 Einstein's photoelectric equation
13.4 Wave–particle duality

Specification reference: 4.5.2, 4.5.3

13.3 Einstein's photoelectric equation

The photoelectric equation is based on two important ideas – the principle of conservation of energy and the quantum physics rule of one-to-one interaction between a photon and an electron.

Einstein's equation

When an electron is emitted from the surface of a metal, we have:

energy of photon = work function of the metal + maximum kinetic energy of emitted electron

or

$$hf = \phi + KE_{max}$$

The electron is loosely held by the attraction of the positive ions of the metal. The work function ϕ is the minimum energy it takes to free an electron. The emitted electrons can collide with other electrons and the positive ions and this is why the electrons emerge with a range of kinetic energies. The maximum KE_{max} is still given by the equation above.

Observations:

- Not a single electron can be emitted when $hf < \phi$. Increasing the intensity just increases the rate of the photons but the energy of individual photons is still less than the work function.
- At the threshold frequency f_0, the kinetic energy of the emitted electrons is zero. Therefore, $hf_0 = \phi$.

Revision tip

$1\ \text{eV} = 1.60 \times 10^{-19}\ \text{J}$

Use units consistently when using the equation $hf = \phi + KE_{max}$

KE_{max} against f graph

The photoelectric equation can be rearranged as

$$KE_{max} = hf - \phi$$

The work function ϕ and Planck constant h can be determined by plotting a graph of KE_{max} against f, see Figure 1.

- The gradient of the straight-line graph is h.
- The intercept with the vertical axis is $-\phi$.
- The intercept with the horizontal axis is the threshold frequency f_0.

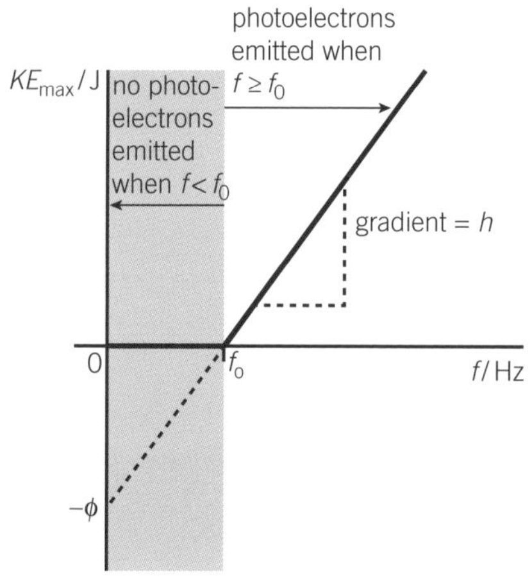

▲ **Figure 1** *The gradient of this graph is always h and is independent of the metal used*

13.4 Wave–particle duality

Electromagnetic waves have a dual nature – they travel as waves and they interact as 'particles' (photons). Louis de Broglie, in 1923, proposed that matter, which includes particles such as electrons, must also have a dual nature.

De Broglie equation

A particle travelling through space with momentum p has an associated wavelength λ given by the de Broglie equation

$$\lambda = \frac{h}{p} \quad \text{or} \quad \lambda = \frac{h}{mv}$$

where h is the Planck constant, m is the mass of the particle, and v is its speed.

Revision tip

The waves associated with moving particles are also known as matter waves. These waves are not electromagnetic waves.

Evidence

The wave-like behaviour of electrons can be demonstrated using an electron diffraction tube. Accelerated electrons pass through a thin sheet of graphite. The separation between the atomic layers of graphite is very similar to the de Broglie wavelength of the electrons. Electrons are diffracted by the 'gaps' between the atoms of graphite and therefore demonstrate wave-like behaviour. Figure 2 shows the diffraction rings produced by electrons having travelled through graphite (or a thin metal foil).

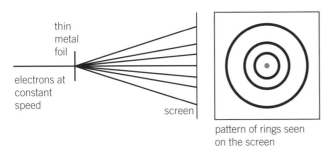

pattern of rings seen
on the screen

▲ **Figure 2** *Electrons are diffracted by the gaps between atoms*

 Worked example: Diffracting people?

Make suitable estimations to explain why a person running through a metre-wide gap in a wall will not be diffracted.

Step 1: Make suitable estimates for quantities required for the de Broglie equation.

mass $m = 70\,\text{kg}$ speed $v = 8.0\,\text{m s}^{-1}$

Step 2: Calculate the de Broglie wavelength.

$$\lambda = \frac{h}{p} = \frac{h}{mv} = \frac{6.63 \times 10^{-34}}{70 \times 8.0}$$

wavelength $= 1.2 \times 10^{-36}\,\text{m} \approx 10^{-36}\,\text{m}$ (2 s.f.)

Step 3: Provide a suitable explanation.

For noticeable diffraction, the wavelength must be similar to the width of the gap.

The person's de Broglie wavelength is 10^{36} times smaller than the width of the gap therefore there will be no diffraction.

Summary questions

1   State one quantity conserved when a photon interacts with an electron. *(1 mark)*

2   A photon has energy $7.2 \times 10^{-19}\,\text{J}$. It removes an electron from a metal of work function $6.9 \times 10^{-19}\,\text{J}$.
    Calculate the maximum kinetic energy of the electron. *(2 marks)*

3   Calculate the maximum speed of the electron in **Q2**. *(2 marks)*

4   The maximum wavelength that produces photoemission from a metal is $2.1 \times 10^{-7}\,\text{m}$.
    Calculate the work function of the metal. *(3 marks)*

5   Electromagnetic radiation of wavelength 320 nm is incident on a metal of work function 2.3 eV.
    Calculate the maximum kinetic energy of the emitted photoelectrons. *(4 marks)*

6   Calculate the de Broglie wavelength of an electron accelerated through a p.d. of 1.5 V. *(4 marks)*

1 Electromagnetic radiation incident on metal ejects electrons from the surface of the metal.

Which statement about the kinetic energy (KE) of the electrons is correct?

A The electrons have the same KE.

B The maximum KE of the electrons depends on the intensity.

C The KE of electrons is always greater than the work function.

D The maximum KE depends on the incident wavelength. *(1 mark)*

2 What is the typical energy of a photon of infrared radiation?

A 4×10^{-24} J   **C** 4×10^{-19} J

B 4×10^{-20} J   **D** 4×10^{-17} J *(1 mark)*

3 The energy of a photon is related to the wavelength λ or the frequency f of the electromagnetic radiation.

Which graph will produce a straight line?

A E against f **B** E against λ **C** $E\lambda$ against f **D** Ef against λ *(1 mark)*

4 Electrons accelerated through a potential difference V have a de Broglie wavelength λ.

What is the wavelength of electrons accelerated through a potential difference of $4V$?

A $\dfrac{\lambda}{4}$ **B** $\dfrac{\lambda}{2}$ **C** 2λ **D** 4λ *(1 mark)*

5 **a** State what is meant by the photoelectric effect. *(1 mark)*

b Electromagnetic radiation incident on a metal ejects electrons from its surface.

Explain this observation in terms of photons and electrons. *(3 marks)*

c A researcher is investigating photoelectric effect using a new material.

Figure 1 shows a graph of maximum kinetic energy KE_{max} of the photoelectrons against frequency f of the incident electromagnetic radiation.

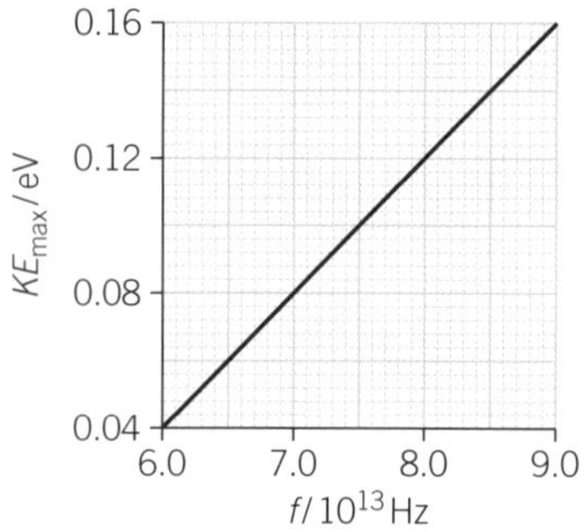

  i Explain why the graph is linear. *(2 marks)*

  ii Use Figure 1 to determine the work function of the material in eV. *(4 marks)*

  iii Use your answer to (ii) to determine the threshold frequency. *(2 marks)*

6 The work function of a metal is 3.7 eV. The metal is charged negatively and then it is illuminated with electromagnetic waves of wavelength 300 nm. Photoelectrons are emitted from the surface of the metal.

a Explain the term work function. *(1 mark)*

b Calculate the maximum kinetic energy, in eV, of the photoelectrons. *(4 marks)*

c Calculate the longest wavelength of electromagnetic radiation that will produce photoelectric effect. *(2 marks)*

7 **a** Explain what is meant by the de Broglie wavelength of an electron. *(2 marks)*

b Fast-electrons can be used to probe into the structure of nuclei. Such electrons have a de Broglie wavelength of about 2.0×10^{-15} m.

Calculate the momentum of the electrons. *(2 marks)*

c Briefly described an experiment that confirms that electrons behave as waves. *(3 marks)*

▲ Figure 1

(graph: KE_{max}/eV on vertical axis, values 0.04, 0.08, 0.12, 0.16; $f/10^{13}$ Hz on horizontal axis, values 6.0, 7.0, 8.0, 9.0)

A1 Physical quantities and units

Units

Most of the physical quantities you come across in your course can be expressed by combinations of six base units – kg, m, s, A, K, and mol.

All derived units can be worked out using an appropriate equation and then multiplying and/or dividing the base units.

Example:

density = mass/volume   mass $\rightarrow$ kg   volume $\rightarrow$ m^3

Therefore, density has units kg/m^3 or kg m^{-3}.

Homogeneous

An equation is homogeneous when the left-hand side has the same units as the right-hand side. A relationship between physical quantities can only be correct if the equation is homogeneous.

Example:

$s = \dfrac{1}{2}at^2$

right-hand side: $a \rightarrow$ m s^{-2}, $t^2 \rightarrow$ s^2, and $\dfrac{1}{2}$ has no unit.

Therefore $\dfrac{1}{2}at^2 \rightarrow$ m s$^{-2} \times$ s^2 or m

left-hand side: $s \rightarrow$ m

The unit m is the same on both sides of the equal sign – the equation is homogeneous.

A2 Recording results and straight lines

Labelling and significant figures

In a table of results, each heading must have the quantity and its unit. The quantity can be represented by a symbol or in words. A slash (solidus /) is used to separate the quantity and its unit, for example, v / m s^{-1} for speed. The labelling of graph axes follows the same rules as for table headings.

Be careful with significant figures in your table of results. The result of a calculation that involves measured quantities has the same number of significant figures as the measurement that has the *smallest* number of significant figures.

Example:

If the distance is 2.12 m (3 s.f.) and time is 3.2 s (2.s.f.), then the speed is written as 0.66 m s^{-1} (2 s.f.).

Graphs

As a general rule, you plot the independent variable, the one you intentionally change in an experiment, on the x-axis, and the dependent variable, the variable which changes as a result, on the y-axis.

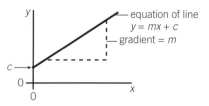

▲ **Figure 1** *Straight-line graph. The gradient of the line is $\frac{\Delta y}{\Delta x}$*

Figure 1 shows a straight-line graph. The equation for a straight line is $y = mx + c$, where m is the gradient and c is the y-intercept. Always use a large triangle to determine the gradient of the straight line.

Sometimes plotting the measured quantities does not produce a straight-line graph. You have to plot data carefully if you want to get a straight line and verify a relationship.

Example:

The equation is $v^2 = 2as$, and you have measured the velocity v and the displacement s. A graph of v against s will be a curve. Plotting v^2 against s should produce a straight line. The gradient of the line will be $2a$, therefore you can determine the acceleration a.

A3 Measurements and uncertainties

Definitions

Remember that no measurement can ever be perfect.

- **Error** (of measurement) is the difference between an individual measurement and the **true** value (or accepted reference value) of the quantity being measured.
- **Random errors** can happen when any measurement is being made. They are measurement errors in which measurements vary unpredictably.
- **Systematic errors** are measurement errors in which the measurements differ from the true values by a consistent amount each time a measurement is made.
- **Accuracy** is to do with how close a measurement result is to the true value.
- **Precision** is to do with how close repeated measurements are to each other.
- The **uncertainty** in the measurement is an interval within which the true value can be expected to lie. The **absolute uncertainty** is approximated as half the range.

Example:

$x = 52 \pm 3\,\text{mm}$

absolute uncertainty $= 3\,\text{mm}$

% uncertainty $= \dfrac{3}{52} \times 100 = 5.8\%$

Uncertainty rules

Rule 1: Adding or subtracting quantities

When you add or subtract quantities in an equation, you add the absolute uncertainties for each value.

Example:

$x = 4.2 \pm 0.3 \qquad y = 3.0 \pm 0.2 \qquad x - y = 1.2 \pm 0.5$

Rule 2: Multiplying or dividing quantities

When you multiply or divide quantities, you add the percentage uncertainties for each value.

Example:

$x = 2.0 \pm 0.3 \qquad y = 1.2 \pm 0.1$

% uncertainty in $xy = \left(\dfrac{0.3}{2.0} + \dfrac{0.1}{1.2}\right) \times 100 = 23\%$

Rule 3: Raising a quantity to a power

When a measurement in a calculation is raised to a power n, your percentage uncertainty is increased n times. The power n can be an integer or a fraction.

Example:

$x = 3.14 \pm 0.13$ % uncertainty in $x^4 = 4 \times \left(\dfrac{0.13}{3.14}\right) \times 100 \approx 17\%$

Graphs

You can show error bars for each plotted point, see Figure 2. The best-fit straight line must pass through all the error bars. You can determine the percentage uncertainty in the gradient by drawing a 'worst-fit' straight line and doing the following calculation:

% uncertainty $= \dfrac{\text{gradient of worst-fit line} - \text{gradient of best-fit line}}{\text{gradient of best-fit line}} \times 100\%$

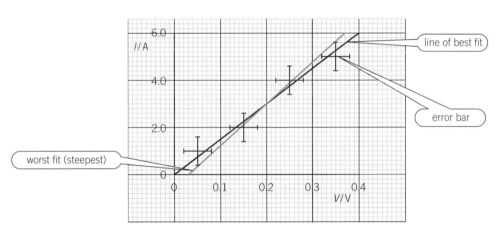

▲ **Figure 2** *Plotted points can have errors bars*

Data, Formulae, and Relationships

The data, formulae, and relationships in this datasheet will be printed for distribution with the examination papers.

Data

Values are given to three significant figures, except where more – or fewer – are useful.

Physical constants

acceleration of free fall	g	9.81 m s^{-2}
elementary charge	e	$1.60 \times 10^{-19} \text{ C}$
speed of light in a vacuum	c	$3.00 \times 10^{8} \text{ m s}^{-1}$
Planck constant	h	$6.63 \times 10^{-34} \text{ J s}$
Avogadro constant	N_A	$6.02 \times 10^{23} \text{ mol}^{-1}$
molar gas constant	R	$8.31 \text{ J mol}^{-1} \text{K}^{-1}$
Boltzmann constant	k	$1.38 \times 10^{-23} \text{ J K}^{-1}$
gravitational constant	G	$6.67 \times 10^{-11} \text{ N m}^2 \text{kg}^{-2}$
permittivity of free space	ε_0	$8.85 \times 10^{-12} \text{ C}^2 \text{N}^{-1} \text{m}^{-2} \text{ (F m}^{-1})$
electron rest mass	m_e	$9.11 \times 10^{-31} \text{ kg}$
proton rest mass	m_p	$1.673 \times 10^{-27} \text{ kg}$
neutron rest mass	m_n	$1.675 \times 10^{-27} \text{ kg}$
alpha particle rest mass	m_α	$6.646 \times 10^{-27} \text{ kg}$
Stefan constant	σ	$5.67 \times 10^{-8} \text{ W m}^{-2} \text{K}^{-4}$

Quarks

up quark	$\text{charge} = +\frac{2}{3}e$
down quark	$\text{charge} = -\frac{1}{3}e$
strange quark	$\text{charge} = -\frac{1}{3}e$

Conversion factors

unified atomic mass unit	$1 \text{ u} = 1.661 \times 10^{-27} \text{ kg}$
electronvolt	$1 \text{ eV} = 1.60 \times 10^{-19} \text{ J}$
day	$1 \text{ day} = 8.64 \times 10^{4} \text{ s}$
year	$1 \text{ year} \approx 3.16 \times 10^{7} \text{ s}$
light year	$1 \text{ light year} \approx 9.5 \times 10^{15} \text{ m}$
parsec	$1 \text{ parsec} \approx 3.1 \times 10^{16} \text{ m}$

Mathematical equations

arc length $= r\theta$

circumference of circle $= 2\pi r$

area of circle $= \pi r^2$

curved surface area of cylinder $= 2\pi rh$

surface area of sphere $= 4\pi r^2$

area of trapezium $= \frac{1}{2}(a + b)h$

volume of cylinder $= \pi r^2 h$

volume of sphere $= \frac{4}{3}\pi r^3$

Pythagoras' theorem: $a^2 = b^2 + c^2$

cosine rule: $a^2 = b^2 + c^2 - 2bc\cos A$

sine rule: $\dfrac{a}{\sin A} = \dfrac{b}{\sin B} = \dfrac{c}{\sin C}$

$\sin\theta \approx \tan\theta \approx \theta$ and $\cos\theta \approx 1$ for small angles

$\log(AB) = \log(A) + \log(B)$

(Note: $\lg = \log_{10}$ and $\ln = \log_e$)

$\log\left(\dfrac{A}{B}\right) = \log(A) - \log(B)$

$\log(x^n) = n\log(x)$

$\ln(e^{kx}) = kx$

Formulae and relationships

Module 2 Foundations of physics

vectors

$$F_x = F\cos\theta$$

$$F_y = F\sin\theta$$

Module 3 Forces and motion

uniformly accelerated motion

$$v = u + at$$

$$s = \frac{1}{2}(u + v)t$$

$$s = ut + \frac{1}{2}at^2$$

$$v^2 = u^2 + 2as$$

force

$$F = \frac{\Delta p}{\Delta t}$$

$$p = mv$$

turning effects

$$\text{moment} = Fx$$

$$\text{torque} = Fd$$

density

$$\rho = \frac{m}{V}$$

pressure

$$p = \frac{F}{A}$$

$$p = h\rho g$$

work, energy, and power

$$W = Fx\cos\theta$$

$$\text{efficiency} = \frac{\text{useful energy output}}{\text{total energy input}} \times 100\%$$

$$P = \frac{W}{t}$$

$$P = Fv$$

springs and materials

$$F = kx$$

$$E = \frac{1}{2}Fx;\ E = \frac{1}{2}kx^2$$

$$\sigma = \frac{F}{A}$$

$$\varepsilon = \frac{x}{L}$$

$$E = \frac{\sigma}{\varepsilon}$$

Module 4 Electrons, waves, and photons

charge

$$\Delta Q = I\Delta t$$

current

$$I = Anev$$

work done

$$W = VQ;\ W = \mathcal{E}Q;\ W = VIt$$

resistance and resistors

$$R = \frac{\rho L}{A}$$

$$R = R_1 + R_2 + \ldots$$

$$\frac{1}{R} = \frac{1}{R_1} + \frac{1}{R_2} + \ldots$$

power

$$P = VI;\ P = I^2R;\ P = \frac{V^2}{R}$$

internal resistance

$$\mathcal{E} = I(R + r);\ \mathcal{E} = V + Ir$$

potential divider

$$V_{out} = \frac{R_2}{R_1 + R_2} \times V_{in}$$

$$\frac{V_1}{V_2} = \frac{R_1}{R_2}$$

waves

$$v = f\lambda$$

$$f = \frac{1}{T}$$

$$I = \frac{P}{A}$$

$$\lambda = \frac{ax}{D}$$

refraction

$$n = \frac{c}{v}$$

$$n \sin\theta = \text{constant}$$

$$\sin C = \frac{1}{n}$$

quantum physics

$$E = hf$$

$$E = \frac{hc}{\lambda}$$

$$hf = \phi + KE_{\text{max}}$$

$$\lambda = \frac{h}{p}$$

Answers to practice questions

Chapter 2

1 C [1]

2 D [1]

3 B [1]

4 B [1]

5 a Velocity is a vector with both magnitude and direction. The direction of travel of the satellite changes therefore its velocity changes. [1]

  b i distance $= \frac{1}{4} \times$ circumference

       $= \frac{1}{4} \times 2\pi \times 2.0 \times 10^7$ [1]

      distance $= 3.1 \times 10^7$ m [1]

  ii displacement = direct distance from A to B [1]

     displacement$^2 = 2 \times (2.0 \times 10^7)^2$ [1]

     displacement $= 2.8 \times 10^7$ m [1]

6 a The force N is 90° to the ramp therefore its component along the ramp is zero. ($N\cos 90° = 0$) [1]

  b component $= 8.0 \cos 60° = 4.0$ N [1]

  c Correct diagram with sides and one of the angles labelled, see below. [2]

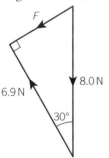

  resultant force $F = \left(8.0^2 - 6.9^2\right)^{\frac{1}{2}}$ [1]

  $F = 4.0$ N [1]

  (Note: The resultant force is the same as the answer to **6b**.)

Chapter 3

1 D [1]

2 C [1]

3 D [1]

4 a Acceleration is the rate of change of velocity. [1]

  b i The velocity of the ball is increasing with time. [1]

    The gradient of the graph is equal to velocity and the gradient is increasing with time. [1]

  ii velocity = gradient [1]

    Tangent drawn at $t = 2.0$ s to determine the gradient. [1]

    velocity $= 1.0$ m s^{-1} (allow ± 0.1 m s^{-1}) [1]

  iii $a = \frac{1.0 - 0}{2.0}$ [1]

    $a = 0.50$ m s^{-2} [1]

5 a $s = ut + \frac{1}{2}at^2$ and $u = 0$. Therefore, $h = \frac{1}{2}at^2$ [1]

  With constant acceleration a, $h \propto t^2$ – therefore, a straight line passing through the origin. [1]

  b gradient $= \frac{g}{2}$ [1]

  gradient $= 5.0$ (allow ± 0.1) [1]

  Therefore, $g = 2 \times 5.0 = 10$ m s^{-2} [1]

  c No change to the gradient of the graph because g is the same for all falling objects on the Earth. [1]

Chapter 4

1 C [1]

2 A [1]

3 D [1]

4 a $a = \frac{200 - 180}{400}$ [1]

  $a = 0.05$ m s^{-2} [1]

  b Both are 90° to the horizontal and therefore each has no component in the horizontal plane. [1]

  c pressure $= \frac{400 \times 9.81}{1.8}$ [1]

  pressure $= 2.2 \times 10^3$ Pa [1]

5 a The sum of the clockwise moments about a point is equal to the sum of the anticlockwise moments about the same point. [1]

  b i mass $= \frac{1800}{9.81}$ [1]

    volume $= \frac{\text{mass}}{\text{density}} = \frac{1800}{9.81 \times 900}$ [1]

    volume $= 0.20$ m^3 [1]

  ii sum of clockwise moments about X = sum of anticlockwise moments about X [2]

    $1800 \times 1.0 = T\cos 45° \times 1.5$ [1]

    $T = 1.7 \times 10^3$ N

  iii The force at X must have a horizontal component that would cancel out the horizontal component of the tension. [1]

6 a The resultant force is zero because the ship is travelling at constant speed. [1]

  b force $= 2 \times 8.6 \times 10^3 \cos 30°$ [2]

    • force $= 1.5 \times 10^4$ N [1]

  c The drag is equal to 1.5×10^4 N because the resultant force on the ship is zero. [1]

  The direction of drag is opposite to the direction of travel. [1]

Chapter 5

1 B [1]
2 C [1]
3 D [1]
4 C [1]
5 a Energy can neither be created nor destroyed. It can just be transferred from one form into another. [1]

   b i loss in GPE = mgh = 0.040 × 9.81 × 0.080
= 3.14×10^{-2} J ≈ 3.1×10^{-2} J [1]

     ii KE = $\frac{1}{2} mv^2 = \frac{1}{2} \times 0.040 \times 0.90^2$
= 1.62×10^{-2} J ≈ 1.6×10^{-2} J [1]

     iii work done = $(3.14 - 1.62) \times 10^{-2}$ J [1]
work done = 1.52×10^{-2} J ≈ 1.5×10^{-2} J [1]

     iv $F \times 0.08 = 1.52 \times 10^{-2}$ [1]
F = 0.19 N [1]

6 a a = (0.21 × 9.81)/(0.80 + 0.21) [1]
a = 2.04 m s^{-2} [1]

   b $v^2 = 2as$ = 2 × 2.04 × 0.50 [1]
KE = $\frac{1}{2} mv^2 = \frac{1}{2} \times 0.80 \times [2 \times 2.04 \times 0.50]$ [1]
KE = 0.816 J ≈ 0.82 J [1]

   c loss in GPE = mgh = 0.21 × 9.81 × 0.50
= 1.03 J ≈ 1.0 J [1]

   d The loss in GPE of the 0.21 kg mass is equal to the KE of *both* the trolley and the falling mass – this is why the answers are not the same. [1]

Chapter 6

1 D [1]
2 D [1]
3 C [1]
4 D [1]
5 a i k = gradient = $\frac{5.0}{0.60}$ [1]
k = 8.3 N m^{-1} [1]

     ii Assume that Hooke's law is obeyed. [1]
$F \propto x$ therefore $\frac{F}{x}$ = constant [1]
$x = 0.60 \times \frac{9.0}{5.0}$ = 1.08 m ≈ 1.1 m [1]

   b Force experienced by each spring = 10 N [1]
extension x of each spring = $\frac{10}{40}$ = 0.25 m [1]
energy stored = $2 \times \left(\frac{1}{2} \times 10 \times 0.25 \right)$ [1]
energy stored = 2.5 J

6 a Young modulus = $\frac{\text{tensile stress}}{\text{tensile strain}}$ [1]

   b i stress = $0.4 \times 10^9 = \frac{16}{A}$ [1]
$A = 4.0 \times 10^{-8}$ m^2 [1]

     ii E = gradient [1]
$E = \frac{0.3 \times 10^9}{2.0 \times 10^{-3}}$ [1]
$E = 1.5 \times 10^{11}$ Pa [1]

     iii The shape does not depend on the dimensions of the material but just on the material itself. [1]
Therefore, there is no change to the shape of the graph. [1]

7 a strain = $\frac{x}{L} = \frac{0.54 \times 10^{-3}}{1.20}$ [1]
strain = 4.5×10^{-4} [1]

   b stress = E × strain = $8.0 \times 10^{10} \times 4.5 \times 10^{-4}$ [1]
stress = 3.6×10^7 Pa [1]
F = stress × A = $3.6 \times 10^7 \times 2.1 \times 10^{-7}$
= 7.56 N [1]
mass = $\frac{F}{g} = \frac{7.56}{9.81}$ = 0.77 kg [1]

Chapter 7

1 B [1]
2 D [1]
3 A [1]
4 D [1]
5 a linear momentum = mass × velocity [1]

   b The resultant force acting on an object is directly proportional to its rate of change of momentum. [1]

   c i change in momentum
= Δp = −0.800 × (4.0 + 6.0)
Δp = (−)8.0 kg m s^{-1} [1]

     ii force = $\frac{\Delta p}{\Delta t} = \frac{8.0}{0.025}$ [1]
force = 320 N [1]

     iii According to Newton's third law, the force acting on the ground is equal and opposite to the force experienced by the object. [1]
Therefore, the direction of the force experienced by the ground is vertically downwards. [1]

6 a impulse = force × time [1]

   b i $F = ma$ therefore the acceleration a is directly proportional to the force F. [1]
Therefore, the acceleration is maximum at t = 0 and it decreases linearly to zero at t = 0.4 s. [1]

     ii change in momentum = impulse = area under graph [1]
increase in momentum
= $\frac{1}{2} \times 6.0 \times 0.4$ = 1.2 kg m s^{-1} [1]
final momentum
= 1.2 + (0.200 × 3.0) = 1.8 kg m s^{-1} [1]
final speed $v = \frac{1.8}{0.200}$ = 9.0 m s^{-1} [1]

7 a Inelastic collision is one in which momentum is conserved but kinetic energy is not. Some of the KE is transferred to other forms. [1]

b i $p = 8.0 \times 10^4 \times 0.50 = 4.0 \times 10^4 \, \text{kg m s}^{-1}$ [1]

ii initial momentum = final momentum [1]

$4.0 \times 10^4 = 12 \times 10^4 \times v$ [1]

$v = 0.33 \, \text{m s}^{-1}$ [1]

iii 1 $\text{KE} = \frac{1}{2} \times 8.0 \times 10^4 \times (0.50^2 - 0.33^2)$ [1]

$\text{KE} = 5.64 \times 10^3 \, \text{J} \approx 5.6 \times 10^3 \, \text{J}$ [1]

2 $\text{KE} = \frac{1}{2} \times 4.0 \times 10^4 \times 0.33^2 = 2.2 \times 10^3 \, \text{J}$ [1]

iv The collision is inelastic with some of the kinetic energy being transferred to heat and sound. [1]

Chapter 8

1 B [1]

2 A [1]

3 C [1]

4 B [1]

5 a The direction of conventional current is the direction in which positive charges travel therefore the direction of this current is to the left. [1]

b i $Q = 0.040 \times 30$ [1]

charge = 1.2 C [1]

ii number of electrons $= \dfrac{1.2}{1.6 \times 10^{-19}}$ [1]

number of electrons $= 7.5 \times 10^{18}$ [1]

6 a $n = 8.5 \times 10^{22} \times 10^6 = 8.5 \times 10^{28} \, \text{m}^{-3}$
$(1 \, \text{cm}^3 = 10^{-6} \, \text{m}^3)$ [1]

b $I = Anev$ [1]

$v = \dfrac{9.5}{\pi \times (0.6 \times 10^{-3})^2 \times 8.5 \times 10^{28} \times 1.6 \times 10^{-19}}$ [1]

$v = 6.2 \times 10^{-4} \, \text{m s}^{-1}$ [1]

c distance $= 6.2 \times 10^{-4} \times 2.0 \times 60$ [1]

distance $= 0.074 \, \text{m}$ [1]

7 a current = rate of flow of charge therefore the gradient is equal to current. [1]

b current $= \dfrac{6.0}{4.0} = 1.5 \, \text{A}$ [1]

c The current is constant at 1.5 A between $t = 0$ and $t = 4.0 \, \text{s}$. [1]

After $t = 4.0 \, \text{s}$, the current is smaller. [1]

Value of current after 4.0 s is 0.50 A. [1]

Chapter 9

1 C [1]

2 B [1]

3 D [1]

4 D [1]

5 a resistance $= \dfrac{\text{potential difference}}{\text{current}}$ [1]

b i $R = \dfrac{3.0}{2.0} = 1.5 \, \Omega$ [1]

ii $\rho = \dfrac{RA}{L}$ [1]

$\rho = \dfrac{1.5 \times \pi \times (0.41 \times 10^{-3})^2}{0.09}$ [1]

$\rho = 8.8 \times 10^{-6} \, \Omega \, \text{m}$ [1]

iii current $= \dfrac{2.5}{1.5} = 1.7 \, \text{A}$ [1]

6 a 12 W is the power of the lamp. [1]

12 J of electrical energy is transferred to heat (and light) per second. [1]

b $I_A = \dfrac{P}{V} = \dfrac{12}{230} = 0.052 \, \text{A}$ [1]

$I_B = \dfrac{P}{V} = \dfrac{36}{230} = 0.157 \, \text{A}$ [1]

total current $= 0.052 + 0.157 \approx 0.21 \, \text{A}$ [1]

c energy in kW h $= \dfrac{12 + 36}{1000 \times 24} = 1.152 \, \text{kW h}$ [2]

cost $= 1.152 \times 10.5 \approx 12 \text{p}$ [1]

7 a The resistance of the LDR increases as the intensity of light decreases. [1]

Therefore, the current in the circuit decreases.

$\left(I = \dfrac{V}{R}, \; V = \text{constant therefore } I \propto \dfrac{1}{R} \right)$ [1]

b For a given supply the power dissipated is greater when the resistance is smaller $\left(P = \dfrac{V^2}{R} \right)$. [1]

Therefore, greater power is dissipated when LDR is in sunlight and its resistance is smaller. [1]

Chapter 10

1 C [1]

2 C [1]

3 A [1]

4 a parallel: $R = (100^{-1} + 330^{-1})^{-1} = 76.7 \, \Omega$ [2]

total $= 76.7 + 100 = 176.7 \, \Omega \approx 180 \, \Omega$ [1]

b p.d. across 330 Ω resistor:
$V = 2.7 \times 10^{-3} \times 330 = 0.891 \, \text{V}$ [1]

current in the 100 Ω resistor:

$I = \dfrac{0.891}{100} = 8.91 \, \text{mA}$ [1]

$\varepsilon = (8.91 + 2.7) \times 10^{-3} \times 176.7$ [1]

$\varepsilon = 2.05 \, \text{V} \approx 2.1 \, \text{V}$ [1]

5 a The sum of the p.d.s in a loop is equal to the sum of the e.m.f.s. [1]

b i $P = \dfrac{V^2}{R}; \; R = \dfrac{3.0^2}{0.60}$ [1]

$R = 15 \, \Omega$ [1]

ii $R = (15^{-1} + 20^{-1})^{-1}$ [1]

$R = 8.57 \, \Omega \approx 8.6 \, \Omega$ [1]

iii $\frac{8.57}{3.0} = \frac{r}{1.5}$ [1]

$r \approx 4.3\,\Omega$ [1]

6 a p.d. across resistor = $0.015 \times 120 = 1.8\,V$ [1]

p.d. across thermistor = $6.0 - 1.8 = 4.2\,V$ [1]

resistance of thermistor = $\frac{4.2}{0.015} = 280\,\Omega$ [1]

b The current in the circuit decreases. [1]

The p.d. across the variable resistor increases. [1]

The sum of the p.d.s must equal $6.0\,V$ therefore the p.d. across the thermistor (voltmeter reading) will decrease. [1]

Chapter 11

1 D [1]

2 C [1]

3 B [1]

4 B [1]

5 a Any two properties from transverse waves: travel in a vacuum, travel at the speed of light c in a vacuum, etc. [2]

b i $\lambda = \frac{c}{f} = \frac{3.0 \times 10^8}{8.0 \times 10^9}$ [1]

$\lambda = 0.038\,m$ [1]

ii Microwaves. [1]

iii time = $\frac{6.3 \times 10^{11}}{3.0 \times 10^8}$ [1]

time = $2100\,s$ (35 minutes) [1]

6 a The speed of light in glass is 1.54 times slower in glass than in vacuum (or air). [1]

b speed = $\frac{3.00 \times 10^8}{1.54} = 1.95 \times 10^8\,m\,s^{-1}$ [1]

c i $1.33 \times \sin 40 = 1.54 \sin r$ [1]

$\sin r = \frac{1.33 \times \sin 40}{1.54}$ [1]

$r = 34°$ [1]

ii Diagram showing refracted light into glass with angle of refraction less than the angle of incidence in water. [1]

Also, reflected light back into water. [1]

Chapter 12

1 D [1]

2 B [1]

3 D [1]

4 C [1]

5 a A progressive wave transfers energy from one place to another through vibrations. [1]

b i The waves emitted from L and R are coherent – they have a constant phase difference. [1]

ii The sound waves at P combine constructively. [1]

The phase difference between the waves is 0° or the path difference is a whole number of wavelengths. [1]

iii **1** $\lambda = \frac{ax}{D} = \frac{0.30 \times 1.4}{5.0}$ [2]

$\lambda = 0.084\,cm$ [1]

2 $v = f\lambda = 4.0 \times 10^3 \times 0.084$ [1]

speed = $340\,m\,s^{-1}$ [1]

6 a $\frac{\lambda}{2} = 30\,cm$; $\lambda = 60\,cm$ [1]

$v = f\lambda = 110 \times 0.60$ [1]

speed = $66\,m\,s^{-1}$ [1]

b The stable pattern of loops disappears. [1]

c $\frac{\lambda}{2} = 20\,cm$; $\lambda = 40\,cm$ [1]

$66 = f \times 0.40$ [1]

frequency = $165\,Hz \approx 170\,Hz$ [1]

Chapter 13

1 D [1]

2 B [1]

3 A [1]

4 B [1]

5 a This effect is the removal of electrons from the surface of a metal using electromagnetic radiation. [1]

b A single photon interacts with a single electron. [1]

Energy is conserved. [1]

energy of photon > work function (or frequency > threshold frequency) [1]

c i $hf = \phi + KE_{max}$ [1]

Equation for a straight-line graph is $y = mx + c$. Therefore, a graph of KE_{max} against f will be linear (with gradient = h and y-intercept = $-\phi$). [1]

ii $f = 9.0 \times 10^{13}\,Hz$ and $KE_{max} = 0.16\,eV$ [1]

$hf = \phi + KE_{max} = 6.63 \times 10^{-34} \times 9.0 \times 10^{13}$
$= \phi + (0.16 \times 1.60 \times 10^{-19})$ [1]

$\phi = 3.407 \times 10^{-20}\,J$ [1]

$\phi = \frac{3.407 \times 10^{-20}}{1.60 \times 10^{-19}} \approx 0.21\,eV$ [1]

iii threshold frequency
$= \frac{\phi}{h} = \frac{3.407 \times 10^{-20}}{6.63 \times 10^{-34}}$ [1]

threshold frequency = $5.1 \times 10^{13}\,Hz$ [1]

6 a This is the minimum energy required by an electron to escape from the surface of the metal. [1]

b $\frac{hc}{\lambda} = \phi + KE_{max}$ [1]

$6.63 \times 10^{-34} \times \dfrac{3.0 \times 10^8}{300 \times 10^{-9}}$

$= (3.7 \times 1.60 \times 10^{-19}) + KE_{max}$ [1]

$KE_{max} = 7.1 \times 10^{-20}\,\text{J}$ [1]

$KE_{max} = \dfrac{7.1 \times 10^{-20}}{1.60 \times 10^{-19}} \approx 0.44\,\text{eV}$ [1]

c $\frac{hc}{\lambda} = 3.7 \times 1.6 \times 10^{-19}$

$\lambda = 6.63 \times 10^{-34} \times \dfrac{3.0 \times 10^8}{3.7 \times 1.6 \times 10^{-19}}$ [1]

$\lambda = 3.4 \times 10^{-7}\,\text{m}$ [1]

7 a A moving electron has wave-like behaviour. [1]

The wavelength λ is given by the de Broglie equation: $\lambda = \dfrac{h}{p}$ [1]

(h = Planck and p = momentum of electron)

b $\lambda = \dfrac{h}{p}$; $p = \dfrac{h}{\lambda} = \dfrac{6.63 \times 10^{-34}}{2.0 \times 10^{-15}}$ [1]

momentum $= 3.3 \times 10^{-19}\,\text{kg m s}^{-1}$ [1]

c Fast-moving electrons are made to travel through a (polycrystalline) metal or graphite. [1]

The electrons are diffracted by the spacing between the atoms. [1]

This is because their de Broglie wavelength is similar to atomic spacing. [1]

Answers to summary questions

2.1/2.2

1 distance = 210×10^3 m = 2.1×10^5 m [1]
2 speed = 1.2×10^{-3} m s^{-1} [1]
3 time = 12×10^{-9} s = 1.2×10^{-8} s [1]
4 diameter in pm = $\dfrac{2.3 \times 10^{-10}}{10^{-12}}$ = 230 pm [1]

   diameter in nm = $\dfrac{2.3 \times 10^{-10}}{10^{-9}}$ = 0.23 nm [1]
5 unit for work done = unit for force × unit for length

   unit for work done = kg m s^{-2} × m [1]

   unit for work done = kg m^2 s^{-2} [1]
6 time = $\dfrac{\text{distance}}{\text{speed}} = \dfrac{150 \times 10^9}{300 \times 10^6}$ [2]

   time = 500 s (8.3 minutes) [1]
7 1 cm = 10^{-2} m therefore 1 cm^2 = $(10^{-2})^2 = 10^{-4}$ m^2 [1]

   area = $620 \times 10^{-4} = 6.2 \times 10^{-2}$ m^2 [1]

2.3/2.4

1 Any two correct scalars (e.g., speed and distance). [1]

   Any two correct vectors (e.g., velocity and momentum). [1]
2 A scalar (13 kg) is being added to a vector (force), which is incorrect. [1]
3 maximum velocity = 20 + 5.0 = 25 m s^{-1} [1]

   minimum velocity = 20 −5.0 = 15 m s^{-1} [1]
4 Correct triangle drawn. [1]

   Correct directions of the arrows and correct labelling. (See below.)

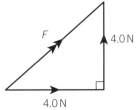

5 $F^2 = 4.0^2 + 4.0^2$ [1]

   $F = 5.7$ N [1]
6 a Correct triangle drawn. [1]

   Correct directions of the arrows and correct labelling. (See below.)

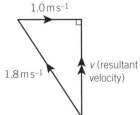

   b $1.8^2 = v^2 + 1.0^2$ [1]

      $v = 1.5$ m s^{-1} [1]

2.5/2.6

1 Horizontally: $v = v_0 \cos\theta = 300 \times \cos 65°$
                              = 127 N ≈ 130 N [1]

   Vertically: $v = v_0 \sin\theta = 300 \times \sin 65°$
                           = 272 N ≈ 270 N [1]
2 acceleration = $9.81 \cos 30° = 8.5$ m s^{-2} [1]

3 $100 = F \sin 50°$ [1]

   $F = \dfrac{100}{\sin 50°} = 130.54$ N ≈ 130 N [1]
4 a $F^2 = 2.0^2 + 3.1^2$ [1]

      $F = \sqrt{13.61} = 3.7$ N [1]

   b $F^2 = (3.0 - 2.0)^2 + 1.0^2$ [1]

      $F = \sqrt{2.0} = 1.4$ N [1]
5 $F^2 = 100^2 + 200^2 - 2 \times 100 \times 200 \times \cos 70°$ [1]

   $F = \sqrt{100^2 + 200^2 - 2 \times 100 \times 200 \times \cos 70°}$ [1]

   $F = 191$ N ≈ 190 N [1]
6 $F^2 = 100^2 + 200^2 - 2 \times 100 \times 200 \times \cos 110°$ [1]

   $F = \sqrt{100^2 + 200^2 - 2 \times 100 \times 200 \times \cos 110°}$ [1]

   $F = 252$ N ≈ 230 N [1]

3.1/3.2

1 $v = \dfrac{1.20}{3.4} = 0.35$ m s^{-2} [1]
2 distance = $20 \times (0.40 \times 3600)$ [1]

   distance = 2.88×10^4 m ≈ 2.9×10^4 m [1]
3 A: Stationary. [1]

   B: Constant velocity and moving away. [1]

   C: Constant velocity and coming back. [1]
4 Correct graph from $t = 0$ to $t = 30$ minutes. [1]

   Correct graph from $t = 30$ minutes to $t = 60$ minutes.

   See below:

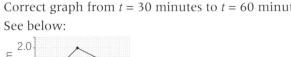

  [1]
5 $t = \dfrac{2\pi r}{v} = \dfrac{2\pi \times 0.020}{5.0 \times 10^5}$ [1]

   $t = 2.5 \times 10^{-7}$ s [1]
6 a The magnitude of the velocities is the same. [1]
      However, the ball is travelling in opposite directions. [1]

   b The velocity is zero. [1]
      The gradient of the graph at $t = 1.0$ s is zero. [1]

3.3/3.4

1 a Zero acceleration or constant velocity. [1]

   b Constant acceleration (starting from a non-zero velocity). [1]

   c Constant deceleration (starting from a non-zero velocity). [1]
2 $a = \dfrac{\Delta v}{\Delta t} = \dfrac{320 - 100}{20}$ [1]

   $a = 11$ m s^{-2} [1]
3 $\Delta v = a\Delta t = 3.0 \times (1.5 \times 60)$ [1]

   $\Delta v = 270$ m s^{-1} [1]
4 $\Delta t = \dfrac{\Delta v}{a} = \dfrac{10}{400}$ [1]

   $\Delta t = 0.025$ s [1]
5 acceleration = gradient [1]

   $a = \dfrac{4.0 - 1.0}{4.0 - 2.0} = 1.5$ m s^{-2} [1]
6 a $0 - 10$ s: Straight line of positive gradient starting from the origin. [1]
      10 s $- 45$ s: Horizontal line with $v = 4.0$ m s^{-1} [1]
      45 s $- 50$ s: Straight line of negative gradient from $v = 4.0$ m s^{-1} to $v = 0$

See below

b distance = area under the graph [1]
distance = $\left(\frac{1}{2} \times 4.0 \times 10\right) + (4.0 \times 35)$
$+ \left(\frac{1}{2} \times 4.0 \times 5.0\right)$ [1]
distance = 170 m [1]
c $a = \frac{\Delta v}{\Delta t} = \frac{0 - 4.0}{5.0}$ [1]
$a = (-)0.80\,\text{m s}^{-2}$ [1]

3.5/3.6

1 $v = u + at = 15 + (-9.81 \times 1.0)$ [1]
$v = 5.2\,\text{m s}^{-1}$ [1]
2 $s = ut + \frac{1}{2}at^2 = (5.0 \times 7.0) + \frac{1}{2} \times 3.0 \times 7.0^2$ [1]
$s = 108.5\,\text{m} \approx 109\,\text{m}$ [1]
3 thinking distance = $16 \times 0.5 = 8.0\,\text{m}$ [1]
braking distance = $\frac{1}{2} \times 16 \times 3.0 = 24\,\text{m}$ [1]
stopping distance = $8.0 + 24 = 32\,\text{m}$ [1]
4 $s = \frac{1}{2}(u + v)t$ [1]
$80 = \frac{1}{2}(10 + 25)t$ [1]
$t = \frac{160}{35} = 4.6\,\text{s}$ [1]
5 $s = ut + \frac{1}{2}at^2$ with $u = 0$ [1]
$100 = \frac{1}{2} \times 9.81 \times t^2$ [1]
$t = 4.5\,\text{s}$ [1]
6 $a = \frac{v - u}{t}$ $v = -14\,\text{m s}^{-1}$ $u = 12\,\text{m s}^{-1}$
$t = 4.0 \times 10^{-3}\,\text{s}$ [1]
$a = \frac{-26}{40 \times 10^{-3}}$ [1]
(Note: change in velocity = $v - u = -14 - 12 = -26\,\text{m s}^{-1}$)
Therefore, magnitude of the acceleration
$a = 6.5 \times 10^3\,\text{m s}^{-2}$ [1]

3.7

1 All objects have a common acceleration of free fall of $9.81\,\text{m s}^{-2}$ [1]
2 $s = ut + \frac{1}{2}at^2$; $u = 0$ and $g = a = 9.81\,\text{m s}^{-2}$ [1]
$s = \frac{1}{2} \times 9.81 \times 0.30^2 = 0.44\,\text{m}$ [1]
3 $s = ut + \frac{1}{2}at^2$; $u = 0$ and $g = a = 1.6\,\text{m s}^{-2}$ [1]
$s = \frac{1}{2} \times 1.6 \times 0.30^2 = 0.072\,\text{m}$ [1]
4 $s = \frac{1}{2}at^2$ therefore $g = \frac{2s}{t^2}$ [1]
$g = \frac{2 \times 2.5}{0.70^2}$ [1]
$g = 10.2\,\text{m s}^{-2} \approx 10\,\text{m s}^{-2}$ [1]
5 $s = \frac{1}{2}at^2$ therefore $g = \frac{2s}{t^2}$ [1]

$g = \frac{2 \times 0.800}{0.403^2}$ [1]
$g = 9.85\,\text{m s}^{-2}$ [1]
6 gradient = $\frac{g}{2}$ [1]
$g = 2 \times \text{gradient} = 2 \times \frac{4.00 - 1.50}{0.82 - 0.31}$ [1]
$g = 9.8\,\text{m s}^{-2}$ (Allow $\pm 0.2\,\text{m s}^{-2}$) [1]
7 absolute uncertainty = $\left(\frac{3}{800} + 2 \times \frac{0.002}{0.403}\right) \times 9.85\,\text{m s}^{-2}$ [2]
absolute uncertainty = $0.13\,\text{m s}^{-2}$ [1]
Therefore, $g = 9.85 \pm 0.13\,\text{m s}^{-2}$ [1]

3.8

1 The horizontal velocity is $5.0\,\text{m s}^{-1}$ [1]
There is no acceleration in the horizontal direction because $g\cos 90° = 0$. [1]
2 displacement = $5.0 \times 0.25 = 1.25\,\text{m} \approx 1.3\,\text{m}$ [1]
3 height = $ut + \frac{1}{2}gt^2$ [1]
height = $0 + \frac{1}{2} \times 9.81 \times 0.70^2$ (vertical motion) [1]
height = $2.4\,\text{m}$ [1]
4 horizontal displacement = $250 \times 0.30 = 75\,\text{m}$ [1]
Vertically $\Rightarrow s = ?$, $u = 0$, $a = 9.81\,\text{m s}^{-2}$, and $t = 0.30\,\text{s}$. [1]
$s = \frac{1}{2} \times 9.81 \times 0.30^2$ [1]
vertical displacement = $0.44\,\text{m}$ [1]
5 $s = ?$ $u = 30\sin 45° = 21.2\,\text{m s}^{-1}$
$v = 0$ $a = -9.81\,\text{m s}^{-2}$ [1]
$s = \frac{v^2 - u^2}{2a} = \frac{0 - (30\sin 45)^2}{2 \times -9.81}$ [1]
$s = 23\,\text{m}$ [1]
6 $t = \frac{0 - 30\sin 45}{9.81} = 4.32\,\text{s}$ (t = time of flight) [1]
horizontal displacement = $30\cos 45° \times 4.32$ [1]
horizontal displacement = $92\,\text{m}$ [1]

4.1/4.2/4.3

1 $a = \frac{400}{1000} = 0.40\,\text{m s}^{-2}$ [1]
2 $a = \frac{400 - 150}{1000}$ [1]
$a = 0.25\,\text{m s}^{-2}$ [1]
3 The car has zero acceleration. [1]
According to $F = ma$, the resultant force acting on the car must be zero. [1]
4 $F \propto a$ for a given mass therefore $a = \frac{65}{20} \times 40$ [1]
$a = 13\,\text{m s}^{-2}$ [1]
5 resultant force $F = \sqrt{(2.0 \times 10^{-15})^2 + (2.0 \times 10^{-15})^2}$ [1]
$F = 2.83 \times 10^{-15}\,\text{N}$ [1]
$a = \frac{2.83 \times 10^{-15}}{9.1 \times 10^{-31}} = 3.1 \times 10^{15}\,\text{m s}^{-2}$ [1]
6 $s = \frac{1}{2}at^2 = \frac{1}{2} \times 3.1 \times 10^{15} \times (20 \times 10^{-9})^2$ [1]
distance = $0.62\,\text{m}$ [1]

4.4

1 The drag force on the truck would be greater because of its large area. [1]
2 The resultant force on the object will be zero. [1]
3 resultant force = weight = $mg = 2.0 \times 9.81 = 20\,\text{N}$
acceleration = $g = 9.81\,\text{m s}^{-2}$ [1]

4 $a = \dfrac{(70 \times 9.81) - 300}{70}$ [2]

$a = 5.5\,\mathrm{m\,s^{-2}}$ [1]

5 $D = 0.80v^2$ [1]

6 drag = weight [1]

$0.80v^2 = 0.100 \times 9.81$ [1]

$v = 1.1\,\mathrm{m\,s^{-1}}$ [1]

4.5/4.6

1 moment = $Fx = 2.0 \times 0.10 = 0.2\,\mathrm{N\,m}$ [1]

2 force = $\dfrac{20}{400}$ [1]

force = $5.0 \times 10^{-2}\,\mathrm{m}$ [1]

3 torque = $3.0 \times 0.15 = 0.45\,\mathrm{N\,m}$ [1]

4 a $1.2 \times 20 = 0.80 \times d_2$ [1]

$d_2 = 30\,\mathrm{cm}$ [1]

b force at pivot $= 1.20 + 0.80 = 1.2\,\mathrm{N}$ [1]

5 Moments about Y:

$Wd_y = S_x(d_x + d_y)$ [1]

$S_x = \dfrac{Wd_y}{d_x + d_y}$ [1]

Moments about X:

$Wd_x = S_y(d_x + d_y)$ [1]

$S_y = \dfrac{Wd_x}{d_x + d_y}$ [1]

6 $S_x = \dfrac{Wd_y}{d_x + d_y} = \dfrac{1.00 \times 1.20}{2.00} = 60\,\mathrm{N}$ [1]

$S_y = \dfrac{Wd_x}{d_x + d_y} = \dfrac{1.00 \times 1.20}{2.00} = 40\,\mathrm{N}$ [1]

4.7

1 Constant velocity implies zero acceleration and therefore the resultant force on the object must be zero. [1]

2 All three forces drawn in the correct direction and form a closed triangle.
All arrows are in the correct directions.
See below.

[1]

3 $F^2 = 12^2 + 5.0^2$ [1]

$F = 13\,\mathrm{N}$ [1]

$\tan\theta = \dfrac{12}{5.0}$ [1]

$\theta = 67°$ [1]

4 $\cos\theta = \dfrac{4.8}{9.6}$ [1]

$\theta = 60°$ [1]

5 $\dfrac{20 \times 9.81}{\sin 140} = \dfrac{T}{\sin 20}$ [2]

$T = 104\,\mathrm{N} \approx 100\,\mathrm{N}$ [1]

6 $2T\cos 20° = 20 \times 9.81$ [1]

$T = \dfrac{20 \times 9.81}{2\cos 20°}$ [1]

$T = 104\,\mathrm{N} \approx 100\,\mathrm{N}$ [1]

4.8/4.9

1 $\rho = \dfrac{m}{V} = \dfrac{350}{0.50} = 700\,\mathrm{kg\,m^{-3}}$ [1]

2 $p = \dfrac{F}{A} = \dfrac{3.0 \times 10^4 \times 9.81}{1.2}$ [1]

pressure = $2.453 \times 10^5\,\mathrm{Pa} \approx 2.5 \times 10^5\,\mathrm{Pa}$ [1]

3 $F = pA = 1.0 \times 10^5 \times (\pi \times 0.15^2)$ [1]

force = $7100\,\mathrm{N}$ [1]

4 total pressure = atmospheric pressure + $h\rho g$ [1]

total pressure = $1.0 \times 10^5 + [3.0 \times 1.0 \times 10^3 \times 9.81]$ [1]

total pressure = $1.3 \times 10^5\,\mathrm{Pa}$ [1]

5 density = $\dfrac{m}{V} = \dfrac{6.0 \times 10^{24}}{\frac{4}{3}\pi \times [6.4 \times 10^6]^3}$ [1]

density = $5.5 \times 10^3\,\mathrm{kg\,m^{-3}}$ [1]

6 $h = \dfrac{p}{\rho g}$ [1]

height = $\dfrac{1.0 \times 10^5}{13.6 \times 1.0 \times 10^3 \times 9.81} = 0.75\,\mathrm{m}$ [1]

5.1/5.2

1 $W = Fx = 20 \times 5.0 = 100\,\mathrm{J}$ [1]

2 Energy is conserved, therefore kinetic energy = $100 - 30 = 70\,\mathrm{J}$ [1]

3 $W = Fx\cos\theta = 100 \times 20 \times \cos 45°$ [1]

work done = $1.4 \times 10^3\,\mathrm{J}$ [1]

4 The weight of the ball is 90° to the horizontal. [1]
There is no work done by the weight because $Fx\cos 90° = 0$ [1]

5 $\cos\theta = \dfrac{W}{Fx} = \dfrac{100}{20 \times 8.0} = 0.625$ [1]

$\theta = \cos^{-1}(0.625) = 51°$ [1]

6 work done by the weight = $2.0 \times 9.81 \times 10$ [1]

work done by drag force = $[2.0 \times 9.81 \times 10] - 120$
$= 76.2\,\mathrm{J}$ [1]

$76.2 = F \times 10$ [1]

$F = 7.6\,\mathrm{N}$ [1]

5.3

1 $E_p = mgh = 1500 \times 9.81 \times 310 = 4.6 \times 10^6\,\mathrm{J}$ [1]

2 $E_k = \dfrac{1}{2}mv^2 = \dfrac{1}{2} \times 1.0 \times 10^{-3} \times (120 \times 10^3)^2$ [1]

$E_k = 7.2 \times 10^6\,\mathrm{J}$ [1]

3 The change in the KE of the stone is the same as the change in its gravitational potential energy (20 J) because energy is conserved. [1]
Assumption: There are no frictional forces and therefore no thermal losses. [1]

4 $v = \sqrt{\dfrac{2E_k}{m}} = \sqrt{\dfrac{2 \times 50 \times 10^3}{1000}}$ [1]

$v = 10\,\mathrm{m\,s^{-1}}$ [1]

5 final KE = $8.0 \times 10^{-21} + \dfrac{1}{2} \times 9.1 \times 10^{-31} \times (1.2 \times 10^5)^2$ [1]

final KE = $1.455 \times 10^{-20}\,\mathrm{J}$ [1]

$v = \sqrt{\dfrac{2E_k}{m}} = \sqrt{\dfrac{2 \times 1.455 \times 10^{-20}}{9.1 \times 10^{-31}}}$ [1]

$v = 1.8 \times 10^5\,\mathrm{m\,s^{-1}}$ [1]

6 a There is loss of GPE and gain in KE from top of swing to the bottom of the swing. [1]
There is gain in GPE and loss in KE from the bottom of the swing to height h. [1]

b $v^2 = 2g(h_0 - h)$ [1]

$v = \sqrt{(2g(h_0 - h))}$ [1]

$v = \sqrt{(2 \times 9.81 \times (3.0 - 0.6))}$ [1]

$v = 6.9 \, \text{m s}^{-1}$ [1]

5.4

1 efficiency $= \dfrac{2.4}{56} \times 100 = 4.3\%$ [1]

2 $W = Pt = 24 \times 3600$ [1]

input energy $= 8.6 \times 10^4 \, \text{J}$ [1]

3 $P = Fv$ $F = \dfrac{P}{v} = \dfrac{6000}{20}$ [1]

force $= 300 \, \text{N}$ [1]

4 input power $= \dfrac{20}{0.25}$ [1]

input power $= 80 \, \text{W}$ [1]

5 a work done = gain in GPE = mgh

$= 0.10 \times 9.81 \times 1.20$ [1]

output power $= \dfrac{0.10 \times 9.81 \times 1.20}{2.4}$ [1]

output power $= 0.49 \, \text{W}$ [1]

b input power $= \dfrac{0.49}{0.12}$ [1]

input power $= 4.1 \, \text{W}$ [1]

6 $P = Fv \propto v^2 \times v$; therefore $P \propto v^3$. [1]

As v is doubled, P will increase by a factor
of $2^3 = 8$ [2]

6.1/6.2

1 $F = kx$ $x = \dfrac{F}{k} = \dfrac{1.2}{25}$ [1]

$x = 4.8 \times 10^{-2} \, \text{m}$ [1]

2 The spring does *not* obey Hooke's law because
increasing the force by a factor of 3 (from 10 N
to 30 N) does not increase the extension by
the same factor. [2]

Extension increases by a factor of $\dfrac{9.2}{2.5} = 3.8$ [1]

3 $E = \dfrac{1}{2}kx^2 = \dfrac{1}{2} \times 120 \times 0.020^2$ [1]

$E = 2.4 \times 10^{-2} \, \text{J}$ [1]

4 $5.4 = \dfrac{1}{2}kx^2 = \dfrac{1}{2} \times 120 \times x^2$ [1]

$x = \sqrt{2 \times \dfrac{5.4}{120}}$ [1]

$x = 0.30 \, \text{m}$ [1]

5 $E = \dfrac{1}{2}kx^2 \propto x^2$ [1]

The stored energy will increase by a factor
of $5^2 = 25$ [1]

6 kinetic energy of ball = elastic potential energy [1]

$\dfrac{1}{2}mv^2 = \dfrac{1}{2}kx^2$ [1]

$v = \sqrt{\dfrac{150 \times 0.09^2}{0.020}}$ [1]

$v = 7.8 \, \text{m s}^{-1}$ [1]

6.3/6.4

1 stress $\to$ Pa; strain $\to$ none; Young modulus $\to$ Pa [1]

2 strain $= \dfrac{x}{L} = \dfrac{0.05}{0.100}$ [1]

strain = 0.50 or 50% [1]

3 stress $= \dfrac{F}{A} = \dfrac{12}{\pi \times (1.0 \times 10^{-3})^2}$ [1]

stress $= 3.82 \times 10^6 \, \text{Pa} \approx 3.8 \times 10^6 \, \text{Pa}$ [1]

4 strain $= \dfrac{\text{stress}}{E}$ [1]

strain $= \dfrac{3.82 \times 10^6}{1.8 \times 10^{11}}$ [1]

strain $= 2.1 \times 10^{-5}$ [1]

5 stress $= \dfrac{F}{A} = \dfrac{5.0 \times 9.81}{\pi \times (0.7 \times 10^{-3})^2} = 3.19 \times 10^7 \, \text{Pa}$ [1]

strain $= \dfrac{x}{L} = \dfrac{3.0 \times 10^{-3}}{3.2} = 9.38 \times 10^{-4}$ [1]

$E = \dfrac{\text{stress}}{\text{strain}} = \dfrac{3.19 \times 10^7}{9.38 \times 10^{-4}}$ [1]

$E = 3.4 \times 10^{10} \, \text{Pa}$ [1]

6 stored energy $= \dfrac{1}{2}Fx$

$= \dfrac{1}{2} \times 5.0 \times 9.81 \times 3.0 \times 10^{-3}$

$= 7.36 \times 10^{-2} \, \text{J}$ [1]

energy stored per unit

volume $= \dfrac{7.36 \times 10^{-2}}{3.2 \times \pi \times (0.7 \times 10^{-3})^2}$ [1]

energy stored per unit volume $= 1.5 \times 10^4 \, \text{J m}^{-3}$ [1]

7.1/7.2

1 According to Newton's third law, the force on the
centre of the Earth is opposite to the weight and
equal to 700 N. [1]

2 $p = mv = 900 \times 30 = 2.7 \times 10^4 \, \text{kg m s}^{-1}$ [1]

3 final velocity $v = at = 9.81 \times 3.0$ [1]

$v = 29.43 \, \text{m s}^{-1}$ [1]

$p = mv = 1.2 \times 29.43 = 35 \, \text{kg m s}^{-1}$ [1]

4 momentum of shell = momentum of cannon [1]

$20 \times 240 = 1200 \times v$ [1]

$v = 4.0 \, \text{m s}^{-1}$ [1]

5 change in momentum $= -mv - mu$ [1]

change in momentum $= -m(v + u)$ [1]

6 final momentum $= (1100 \times 30) - 1.3 \times 10^4$ [1]

$1100v = 2.0 \times 10^4$ [1]

$v = 18 \, \text{m s}^{-1}$ [1]

7 a total initial momentum = total final
momentum [1]

$0.040 \times 80 = 0.340 \times v$ [1]

$v = 9.4 \, \text{m s}^{-1}$ [1]

b loss in KE $= \dfrac{1}{2} \times 0.040 \times 80^2$

$- \dfrac{1}{2} \times 0.340 \times 9.4^2$ [1]

loss in KE $= 110 \, \text{J}$ [1]

7.3/7.4/7.5

1 impulse = change in momentum $= 0.12 \, \text{kg m s}^{-1}$ [1]

2 $\Delta p = 900 \times (10 - 30) = -1.8 \times 10^4 \, \text{kg m s}^{-1}$ [1]

force $= \dfrac{\Delta p}{\Delta t} = \dfrac{1.8 \times 10^4}{5.0}$ [1]

force $= 3.6 \times 10^3 \, \text{N}$ [1]

3 impulse = area under the graph $= \dfrac{1}{2} \times 3000 \times 4.0$ [1]

impulse $= 6000 \, \text{N s}$ [1]

4 change in momentum = impulse $= 6000 \, \text{kg m s}^{-1}$

$1000 \times \Delta v = 6000$ [1]

change in velocity $= 6.0 \, \text{m s}^{-1}$ [1]

5 $\Delta p = -0.040 \times (30 + 30) = 2.4 \, \text{kg m s}^{-1}$ [1]

force $= \dfrac{\Delta p}{\Delta t} = \dfrac{2.4}{2.0 \times 10^{-3}}$ [1]

force $= 1.2 \times 10^3 \, \text{N}$ [1]

6 The final momentums p_1 and p_2 add vectorially
to give a resultant momentum equal to the initial
momentum p in the x-direction. [1]
Correct diagram showing p_1, p_2, and p, with
correct angles shown. [2]
See below.

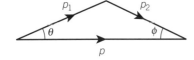

8.1/8.2

1 Electrons in a metal and ions in electrolytes. [1]

2 a This charge is half the charge on an electron,
which is not possible. The student is incorrect. [1]

  b $I = \dfrac{\Delta Q}{\Delta t} = \dfrac{12}{60}$ [1]
  current = 0.20 A [1]

3 charge = $8 \times 1.60 \times 10^{-19}$ [1]
charge = 1.28×10^{-18} C [1]

4 charge = $I \times \Delta t = 0.020 \times (4.0 \times 3600)$ [1]
charge = 288 C $\approx$ 290 C [1]

5 number of electrons = $\dfrac{288}{1.60 \times 10^{-19}}$ [1]
number of electrons = 1.8×10^{21} [1]

6 $I = \dfrac{\Delta Q}{\Delta t} = \dfrac{10^6 \times 1.60 \times 10^{-19}}{60}$ [1]
current = 2.7×10^{-15} A [1]

8.3/8.4

1 The same number of 2 billion electrons would leave
the point because of Kirchhoff's first law and the
conservation of charge. [1]

2 a 1 A   **b** 2 A   **c** 7 A [3]

3 $v \propto I$ therefore as the current decreases by a
factor of 4, the mean drift velocity will also
decrease by the same factor. [1]
mean drift velocity = 0.5 mm s^{-1} [1]

4 $I \propto \dfrac{1}{A}$ [2]
As electrons travel from B to A, the cross-sectional
area of the conductor increases therefore the mean
drift velocity of the electrons decreases. [1]

5 number of electrons = N × volume
= $8.5 \times 10^{28} \times [1.0 \times 10^{-2} \times \pi \times (0.5 \times 10^{-3})^2]$ [1]
number of electrons = 6.7×10^{20} [1]

6 $v = \dfrac{I}{Aen} = \dfrac{3.0 \times 10^{-6}}{[1.0 \times 10^{-3}]^2 \times 1.6 \times 10^{-19} \times 5.0 \times 10^{28}}$ [2]
$v = 3.8 \times 10^{-10}$ m s^{-1} [1]

9.1/9.2/9.3

1 Any two sources of e.m.f. (e.g., chemical cell,
solar cell, thermocouple, etc.) [1]

2 $V = \dfrac{W}{Q} = \dfrac{20}{4.0}$ [1]
$V = 5.0$ V [1]

3 $W = \mathcal{E}Q = 100 \times 60$ [1]
$W = 6000$ J [1]

4 $W = VQ = 1000 \times 1.6 \times 10^{-19}$ [1]
$W = 1.6 \times 10^{-16}$ J [1]

5 charge = $I\Delta t = 0.25 \times 30 = 7.5$ C [1]
$W = VQ = 6.0 \times 7.5 = 45$ J [1]
rate of energy transfer = $\dfrac{45}{30} = 1.5$ J s^{-1} [1]

6 $eV = \dfrac{1}{2}mv^2$ [1]

$v = \sqrt{\dfrac{2 \times 10 \times 10^3 \times 1.6 \times 10^{-19}}{1.67 \times 10^{-27}}}$ [1]
$v = 1.4 \times 10^6$ m s^{-1} [1]

9.4/9.5/9.6

1 Any one from: diode, LED, and filament lamp. [1]

2 $V = IR = 120 \times 0.030 = 3.6$ V [1]

3 The p.d. is also doubled, but resistance,
which is $\dfrac{\text{p.d.}}{\text{current}}$, remains the same. [1]

4 $R = \dfrac{V}{I}$ so when $I = 0$ the resistance R will be
a very large value (infinite). [1]

5 final current = $\dfrac{2.1}{20} = 0.1050$ A [1]
initial current = $\dfrac{1.9}{200} = 0.0095$ A [1]
change in current = 0.1050 − 0.0095
= 0.096 A (2 s.f.) [1]

6 $I = Anev$ therefore number density $n \propto$ current I. [1]
percentage change = $\dfrac{0.1050 - 0.0095}{0.0095} \times 100$
= 1000% [1]

9.7/9.8/9.9

1 $R \propto L$ therefore the resistance increases
by a factor of 4. [1]
resistance = $2.3 \times 4 = 9.2\,\Omega$ [1]

2 $A = 1.0$ m^2 and $L = 1.0$ m [1]
$R = \dfrac{\rho L}{A} = \dfrac{2.7 \times 10^{-8} \times 1.0}{1.0} = 2.7 \times 10^{-8}\,\Omega$ [1]

3 $R = \dfrac{\rho L}{A} = \dfrac{1.6 \times 10^{-8} \times 1.00}{1.2 \times 10^{-6}}$ [1]
$R = 0.013\,\Omega$ [1]

4 $R = \dfrac{\rho L}{A} = \dfrac{2.7 \times 10^{-8} \times 1000}{\pi \times 0.010^2}$ [2]
$R = 0.086\,\Omega$ [1]

5 0 °C to 20 °C
% decrease = $\dfrac{3.5 - 1.8}{3.5} \times 100 \approx 50\%$ [1]
20 °C to 40 °C
% decrease = $\dfrac{1.8 - 1.0}{1.8} \times 100 \approx 40\%$ [1]
There is a smaller % change in the resistance as
temperature increases. [1]

6 $R \propto \dfrac{L}{A}$ [1]
The volume of the wire remains constant,
so when L is 10 times longer, the area
A is 10 times smaller. [1]
$R = 12 \times \dfrac{10}{0.1} = 1200\,\Omega$ [1]

9.10/9.11

1 J s^{-1} [1]

2 $I = \dfrac{P}{V} = \dfrac{2000}{240}$ [1]
$I = 8.3$ A [1]

3 $P = \dfrac{V^2}{R} = \dfrac{240^2}{100}$ [1]
$P = 580$ W [1]

4 cost = $3.0 \times 4.0 \times 8.1$ [1]
cost = 97p [1]

5 $W = 60 \times (10 \times 3600)$ [1]
$W = 2.16 \times 10^6$ J $\approx 2.2 \times 10^6$ J [1]

6 $R = \dfrac{V^2}{P} = \dfrac{12^2}{36}$ [1]
$R = 4.0\,\Omega$ [1]

7 energy = p.d. × charge, and current = $\frac{charge}{time}$ [1]

power = $\frac{energy}{time}$ = $\frac{charge \times p.d.}{time}$ [1]

power = $\frac{charge}{time}$ × p.d = current × p.d.,

therefore $P = VI$ [1]

8 The volume of the wire is the same, so as the length is doubled the cross-sectional area is halved. [1]

$R \propto \frac{L}{A}$ therefore the resistance of the wire is quadrupled. [1]

$P = \frac{V^2}{R}$. The p.d. provided by the power supply is the same. The power dissipated decreases by a factor of 4 because $P \propto \frac{1}{R}$ [1]

The power dissipated is $\frac{10}{4}$ = 2.5 W [1]

10.1/10.2/10.3

1 series: R = 120 × 2 = 240 Ω [1]
parallel: R = $(120^{-1} + 120^{-1})^{-1}$ = 60 Ω [2]

2 p.d. = $\frac{6.0}{10}$ = 0.60 V [1]

3 R = 2.0 + 1.0 + 7.0 = 10.0 Ω [1]
total e.m.f. = 3.0 + 2.0 = 5.0 V [1]

4 current = $\frac{5.0}{10}$ = 0.50 A [1]
$V = IR$ = 0.50 × 7.0 [1]
V = 3.5 V [1]

5 $\frac{1}{R} + \frac{1}{100} = \frac{1}{70}$ [1]

$\frac{1}{R} = \frac{1}{70} - \frac{1}{100} = \frac{30}{7000}$ [1]

$R = \frac{7000}{30}$ = 233 Ω ≈ 230 Ω [1]

6 As temperature decreases, the resistance of the thermistor increases. [1]
Therefore, the current I in the circuit decreases. [1]
$V = IR$; since R is constant at 100 Ω, the p.d. across this resistor will decrease. [1]

10.4/10.5/10.6

1 The 'lost volts' is the p.d. across the internal resistance. [1]

2 There is a p.d. across the internal resistor because of the current in the circuit. [1]
There is a p.d. of 0.4 V across the internal resistance therefore the terminal p.d. cannot be equal to the e.m.f. [1]

3 $I = \frac{1.0}{2.0}$ = 0.050 A [1]

$r = \frac{0.4}{0.05}$ = 8.0 Ω [1]

4 $V = \frac{R_2}{R_1 + R_2} \times V_{in} = \frac{68}{100 + 68} \times 1.5$ [1]
V = 0.61 V [1]

5 $V_{out} = \frac{R_2}{R_1 + R_2} \times V_{in} = \frac{4R}{R + 4R} V_{in}$ [1]
$V_{out} = 0.80V_{in}$ [1]

6 The total resistance of the voltmeter and the 68 Ω thermistor in parallel would be less than 68 Ω. [1]
The total resistance of the circuit would be less and the current in the circuit would be greater. [1]

There is a greater p.d. across the variable resistor and therefore the p.d. across the thermistor would be less (than 0.61 V). [1]

11.1/11.2

1 A frequency of 10 Hz means 10 wavelengths passing through a point per second or 10 oscillations of a medium particle per second. [1]

2 The distance travelled is 2.0 cm in one period. [1]

3 $v = f\lambda$ = 30 × 0.04 = 1.2 m s^{-1} [1]

4 $\lambda = \frac{v}{f} = \frac{340}{150} \times 10^3$ [1]
λ = 2.3 × 10^{-3} m [1]

5 a separation = 0.5λ [1]
Therefore, phase difference = 180° (or π rad) [1]
b separation = 0.75λ [1]
Therefore, phase difference = 270° (or $\frac{3\pi}{2}$ rad) [1]

6 $\frac{x}{20} \times 360$ = 300 [1]
x = 17 cm [1]

11.3/11.4

1 Speed, wavelength, and frequency all remain the same. [1]

2 Sound is a longitudinal wave, and not a traverse wave, so it cannot be polarised. [1]

3 a The wavelength of 500 nm is much smaller than 3.0 cm, so very little diffraction. [1]
b The wavelength of 3.0 cm is similar to 3.0 cm, so there is diffraction. [1]

4 Speed or wavelength. [1]

5 Correct diagram showing the curving around of wavefronts at the edge of the obstacle, see below.

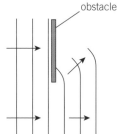
obstacle

[1]

6 The wavelength is longer in water. [1]
The speed $v = f\lambda$ and frequency f remain constant. [1]
Therefore, this implies that the speed of light in water is greater than that in glass. [1]

11.5/11.6/11.7

1 power → [W] and intensity → [W m^{-2}] [1]

2 They can be polarised because they are all transverse waves. [1]

3 intensity ∝ amplitude^2 [1]
Therefore, the intensity decreases by a factor of 4 when the amplitude is halved. [1]

4 $\lambda = \frac{c}{f} = \frac{3.0 \times 10^8}{1.5 \times 10^{17}}$ = 2.0 × 10^{-9} m [2]
The electromagnetic waves must be X-rays (according to Figure 1). [1]

5 $P = 4\pi r^2 \times I$ [1]
$P = 4\pi \times (1.5 \times 10^{11})^2 \times 1050$ [1]
P = 3.0 × 10^{26} W [1]

6 incident power = $1050 \times 1.2 = 1.26 \times 10^3$ W [1]
output power = $0.20 \times 1.26 \times 10^3 = 252$ W [1]
number of panels = $\frac{1000}{252} = 4.0$ [1]

11.8/11.9

1 The refractive index of vacuum is 1. [1]

2 $n = \frac{c}{0.5c} = 2.0$ [1]

3 The refractive index of air is less than the refractive index of glass (1.5). [1]
The statement is incorrect because light has to travel from glass in the direction of air for TIR. [1]

4 $v = \frac{3.0 \times 10^8}{1.50}$ [1]
$v = 2.0 \times 10^8$ m s^{-1} [1]

5 $n_1 \sin\theta_1 = n_2 \sin\theta_2$; $1.00 \times \sin 70° = N \times \sin 35°$ [1]
$n = 1.64$ [1]

6 $n_1 \sin\theta_1 = n_2 \sin\theta_2$
$2.42 \times \sin C = 1.00 \times \sin 90°$ [1]
$\sin C = \frac{1.00}{2.42} = 0.413$ [1]
$C = 24°$ [1]

12.1/12.2/12.3

1 Sources that emits waves with a constant phase difference. [1]

2 The path difference must be a whole number of wavelengths or the phase difference must be zero. [2]

3 a path difference = $11.0 - 7.0 = 4.0$ cm [1]
This is equal to two whole wavelengths therefore constructive interference. [1]

  b path difference = $7.2 - 6.2 = 1.0$ cm [1]
This is equal to half a wavelength therefore destructive interference. [1]

4 $\lambda = \frac{ax}{D} = \frac{0.10 \times 10^{-3} \times 3.1 \times 10^{-2}}{6.20}$ [1]
$\lambda = 5.0 \times 10^{-7}$ m [1]

5 $\lambda \propto x$ therefore $\lambda = \frac{4.1}{5.2} \times 650$ [1]
$\lambda = 510$ nm [1]

6 uncertainty in $a = \pm 0.01$ mm, uncertainty in $x = \pm 0.1$ cm, and uncertainty in $D = \pm 0.01$ m [1]
fractional uncertainty in λ
$= \frac{0.01}{0.10} + \frac{0.1}{3.1} + \frac{0.1}{6.20} = 0.134$ [1]
absolute uncertainty in $\lambda = (5.0 \times 10^{-7}) \times 0.134$
$= 0.7 \times 10^{-7}$ m [1]

12.4/12.5/12.6

1 The phase difference is zero. [1]

2 The separation between node and antinode is $\frac{\lambda}{4}$ [1]
wavelength = $4 \times 10 = 40$ cm [1]

3 The microwaves are reflected off the metal plates. [1]
The superposition of these reflected microwaves and those coming directly from the transmitter produce the stationary wave. [1]

4 $\frac{\lambda}{2} = 28$ [1]
$\lambda = 2 \times 28 = 56$ cm [1]
$v = f\lambda = 60 \times 0.56 = 34$ m s^{-1} [1]

5 length of tube = $\frac{\lambda}{4} = 30$ [1]
$\lambda = 4 \times 30 = 120$ cm [1]
$f = \frac{v}{\lambda} = \frac{340}{1.20} = 280$ Hz [1]

6 $\lambda = \frac{v}{f} = \frac{340}{500} = 0.68$ m [1]
length of tube = $3\frac{\lambda}{2} = 0.68$ [1]
$\lambda = 0.45$ m [1]

13.1/13.2

1 joule (J) [1]

2 $100\,\text{eV} = 100 \times 1.60 \times 10^{-19} = 1.60 \times 10^{-17}$ J [1]

3 1000 eV [1]

4 The energy of a photon of visible light must be less than the work function of the metal. [1]

5 $\lambda = \frac{hc}{E} = \frac{6.63 \times 10^{-34} \times 3.00 \times 10^8}{8.0 \times 10^{-19}}$ [2]
$\lambda = 2.5 \times 10^{-7}$ m [1]

6 $E = \frac{hc}{\lambda} = \frac{6.63 \times 10^{-34} \times 3.00 \times 10^8}{560 \times 10^{-9}} = 3.552 \times 10^{-19}$ J [2]
number of photons per second = $\frac{0.040}{3.552} \times 10^{-19}$ [1]
number of photons per second = 1.1×10^{17} s^{-1} [1]

7 energy of photon:
$E = \frac{hc}{\lambda} = \frac{6.63 \times 10^{-34} \times 3.00 \times 10^8}{400 \times 10^{-9}} = 4.97 \times 10^{-19}$ J [2]
work function: $\phi = 4.30 \times 1.60 \times 10^{-19}$
$= 6.88 \times 10^{-19}$ J [1]
The photon energy is less than the work function, therefore no emission of photoelectrons. [1]

13.3/13.4

1 Energy. [1]

2 $KE_{max} = (7.2 - 6.9) \times 10^{-19}$ [1]
$KE_{max} = 3.0 \times 10^{-20}$ J [1]

3 $\frac{1}{2}mv^2 = 3.0 \times 10^{-20}$
$\frac{1}{2} \times 9.11 \times 10^{-31} \times v^2 = 3.0 \times 10^{-20}$ [1]
$v = 2.6 \times 10^5$ m s^{-1} [1]

4 work function = energy of photon = $\frac{hc}{\lambda}$ [1]
work function = $6.63 \times 10^{-34} \times \frac{3.00 \times 10^8}{2.1 \times 10^{-7}}$ [1]
work function = 9.5×10^{-19} J [1]

5 energy of photon:
$E = \frac{hc}{\lambda} = \frac{6.63 \times 10^{-34} \times 3.00 \times 10^8}{320 \times 10^{-9}} = 6.22 \times 10^{-19}$ J [2]
work function:
$\phi = 2.3 \times 1.60 \times 10^{-19} = 3.68 \times 10^{-19}$ J [1]
$KE_{max} = (6.22 - 3.68) \times 10^{-19}$ J $\approx 2.5 \times 10^{-19}$ J [1]

6 $\frac{1}{2} \times 9.11 \times 10^{-31} \times v^2 = 1.5 \times 1.60 \times 10^{-19}$ [1]
$v = 7.26 \times 10^5$ m s^{-1} [1]
$\lambda = \frac{h}{mv} = \frac{6.63 \times 10^{-34}}{9.11 \times 10^{-31} \times 7.26 \times 10^5}$ [1]
$\lambda = 1.0 \times 10^{-9}$ m [1]